WILLIAM

Rosemary Attlee

A mother's account
of her son's struggle
against cancer

HIGHLAND BOOKS

To William

Blessed is the man whose strength is in thee: in whose
heart are thy ways. Who going through the vale of misery
use it for a well: and the pools are filled with water.
                                        Psalm 84, verses 5, 6

Printed in Great Britain for
HIGHLAND BOOKS
6 The White House, Beacon Road,
Crowborough, East Sussex TN6 1AB
by Richard Clay Ltd, Bungay, Suffolk

Contents

'I have found *William's Story* deeply moving. It is a testimony to the amazing grace of God how both were able to keep right on through his illness and also because of the advanced spiritual insights that were given to William. I pray that it will be an inspiration to very many people and especially parents who find themselves in the same situation. This book cannot but redound to the glory of God.'

Bishop Morris Maddocks

1: A time to die

I was alone in the centre aisle of St. Peter's, Sandwich. We had come off the beach and I had gone in to look round while the others were shopping. It was very quiet; a seldom-used church, shortly to be closed; but it was there that God told me how long my seventeen year old son William was going to live.

For six months we had known he was suffering from leukaemia. Doctors had given various opinions on his expectation of life, ranging from weeks to years. That very morning our family doctor had warned me to be prepared for his final illness to start at any time. Watching his affectionate horseplay with our other children on the beach that afternoon, the familiar knife had turned in my heart as I wondered how long all those young lives were to be unclouded.

I stood there desperately praying, agonised at the uncertainty. With the whole strength of my being I implored to know more. I implored that God would overcome the communication gap and give me a time span to live with. In the instant there seemed to be agreement: if I happened to be standing on a memorial stone I could read that as a sign. I looked slowly down to a 19th century inscription at my feet. It commemorated a young man aged twenty and a few weeks. The experience was so vivid I never forgot what I had learned. When William reached his twentieth birthday, three years later, and started the weeks of his final illness, I sometimes wished I could go back to Sandwich and see how long there was to go, but I couldn't leave him. It was six months after his death before I steeled myself to go back and have another look to see if the inscription had been exact to the very week. We searched the centre aisle, and then the whole floor, but there was no stone.

When William became ill, David and I had been farming in Kent for thirteen singularly happy years; he had just started teaching part time at the local secondary school, to help out our farming income. We had a family of five to bring up. William and his two elder sisters were my children from an unhappy first marriage. When we married William was four and scarcely knew his father, so David had filled a need in his and his sisters' lives and there was a strong bond between them. We also had a boy and girl of our own who were twelve and ten. So William held a strategic place in our family, between the two elder girls and his young half brother and sister. His good humour gave them and us a lot of pleasure.

You wouldn't have called us a christian family. David had always been God fearing but he couldn't make up his mind about Christ. I had committed myself to Him about ten years before, but David seemed to have by nature a great deal more love and unselfishness. It was he who used to round the family up and take them off to church until, as they got into their teens, they opted out.

I lived very much for my children and missed them when they were away at school. William was the one I worried about least; nature seemed to have blessed him with a double share of health, energy and joie de vivre. He was naturally athletic so he enjoyed games which compensated him in the early years for being less interested in the academic side of school life.

It must have been round about ten that night, six months before, when the telephone rang and I heard from William's school doctor that he had been taken to hospital after playing in a school match. He was suffering from a crippling pain in the hip and it was thought he might have leukaemia. I remember I had had my bath and was lying on top of my bed under the eiderdown as he talked, and how I grew cold and my legs started to tremble and shake by themselves. Conclusive results were expected the following afternoon, he said. But the tests looked bad. William was being moved to hospital in Aberdeen.

The next day crawled by as we waited for news. All the family were at home so the telephone rang constantly, and each time it did my heart lurched. We had two young men friends of the girls staying in the house so life and meals had to go on normally. It was a relief to be able to shut myself into my bedroom with the vacuum cleaner which drowned my sobs as I worked methodically up and down. Sleepers on the night train had already been booked and we were almost packed when the news came through. The tests were positive. Before we left I rang my cousin John in his vicarage in Highbury because I knew that he and his wife Sally and their friends would pray — I had to ask him to ring my parents as I found I couldn't talk for tears. We shared the appalling news with Liz, our eldest, then twenty, and left her in charge of the children, house and animals. It was natural to turn to her in our shock as she was always the one we relied on. I wished later I hadn't given her such a heavy burden to carry for so long. I remember her generously lending me her elegant new black boots in which to face the cold winds of Aberdeen.

I have always loved catching the night train north (the fares were much lower then); the noise of diesel engines and all the drama and bustle of King's Cross after dark; the ritual search for one's name on the reservation lists; the satisfaction of finding the narrow cabin with its austere bunks, folded blankets and concealed wash stands containing tiny immaculate squares of soap. This time the very sameness of it all seemed to emphasise the hideous vacuum which had grown up round us, taking away the reality of our surroundings and isolating us with our pain.

In between snatches of sleep, as we jolted and rattled

7

through the night, I think I was searching for some comfort with which to face the next day. I remember thinking, if only I could feel God's love, then I wouldn't feel so alone. I don't want just to believe he loves me, I want to feel it. I remember waking next morning, not knowing where I was for a second, and then wishing it were all a dream; or that time would go back just one day and two nights, and erase what we had heard — or stand still for ever. But light poured under the blind on the window illuminating every bristle in the upholstery on the side of the bunk, which stared inimicably back, level with my eyes, horribly real and quite incapable of change. That pattern remains in my mind as one of the most vivid memories of the journey.

We changed trains, reached Aberdeen in the early afternoon and took a taxi from outside the station. My heart sank as it turned in through the gates of the hospital and pulled up near the main entrance. I wondered how I could steel myself to get out, walk across the concrete, up the steps, into those doors. I found myself thinking surprisingly, it's only because God loves you that you're going to be able to do it and talk calmly to the doctors in there . So in we went.

The smell of hospital wafted out as we pushed open the doors. We were taken to a small clinical waiting room where we sat in total silence until the Specialist arrived. It was a short interview with that concerned Scottish specialist. William had about ten days to live unless he reacted favourably to the course of treatment which had just started. He was no longer in much pain, and had been told only that he was suffering from an acute form of anaemia. If he reacted favourably it was hoped to get him well enough to go home, where he might live for a few more months. I remember he ended by congratulating us on our 'magnificent adjustment'. I expect he had not been looking forward to that interview either: I always felt he was a caring man.

We found William in a side ward looking very young and clean in his hospital pyjamas. Not very communicative about his illness, immensely pleased that we had arrived. We spent a superficially happy time together. David had a small screw-driver in his pocket, a constant farm companion, and was soon altering the height of William's bed table and adjusting parts of the bed. Now that we were together life took a great leap into normality. We were able to be with him until it was time to find somewhere to stay, and then to see David off on the night train home. He had to go back to his teaching, the livestock and the children.

We consulted the young ward sister about places to stay. I couldn't afford to stay for long in a hotel. She advised me to try the Red Cross Hostel, so we were soon knocking on its door. The proprietress was not over joyed to find an importunate traveller on her doorstep but eventually she took me in. I left my case in an empty double room.

We had something to eat in a cafe before David caught the train south. Standing watching its rear light disappearing into the darkness I felt terribly alone. I know it was hard for him as well, and he had two people to grieve for. Then back through the freezing streets to my room in the hostel. I flung myself on my knees on the brown linoleum, numb with grief and fatigue; it was more an S.O.S. than a prayer. Then I climbed into the iron bed, which must have borne the weight of many distressed women in its time, and started the first of many nights under its covering of knitted squares.

2: Take up thy cross

Next morning the Red Cross Hostel revealed itself, very cold, very clean. There was an air of brisk austerity about it; the brown linoleum shone like glass, as if determined that the feet of the sad and necessitous should leave no trace. There were four other women staying there; three kindly fishermen's wives from the Shetland Islands, waiting for the wind to drop and the ferry to make the crossing back. They had been down for hospital appointments. Also a little spinster lady from a village on the island 'where there were no streets'. She was having a course of radiation therapy which sometimes left her very sick. She was a most peaceful woman. Once we were discussing my and her future plans. I remember now the light in her eyes and whole face when she glanced up and said, 'The Lord will take care of those.' I heard she died a few months later.

I spent the greater part of each day with William. On the first I settled self-affacingly on a chair in the corner of the room, determined to hold my place in spite of all possible regulations; but the staff were kind. I never felt unwelcome. We were really very cheerful together, finding every possible way to pass the time. We even made a few doomed attempts at the Times crossword. I scoured the bookshops for light thrillers, and launched myself into knitting a vast fisherman's jersey — so I sat and knitted while he slept, or read. I was very much in the dark about his treatment or how he was reacting; not much information was offered and I didn't ask for any. Pills alternated with injections; one I remember because he had to wear a tight rubber band round his forehead to prevent it destroying his hair. Another time I arrived to see him paper white with two doctors, two nurses and a transfusion set up. It wasn't the crisis I feared. I used to bring staler bread to throw to the seagulls slicing through the cold sky above his window, until I found he wanted to eat the bread himself. The matron on her rounds explained that this was a reaction to the treatment; she asked him what he liked to eat best and said, whatever it was, he could order it from the kitchen. I knew she was making an exception because he had such a short time to live. I told William it was on account of his charm in the hospital pyjamas. We had delightful fantasies of salmon – game – even venison – after all, we were in Scotland! We awaited supper with some anticipation, but no amount of kindness had been able to transform institutional cookery. The 'steak' resembled a four inch square of boiled meat which, as William said, looked as if it had been chewed already! His appetite abated in the next few days, but we always felt kindly towards the Matron.

At that time the grey, snow swept skies and grey granite buildings of Aberdeen entirely suited my mood. I was grateful for anonymity as I passed through the streets and cafes. People were friendly, and interesting in their difference from the people in the south, but were not curious. I didn't have to explain why I had chosen to visit. It was easier eating in cafes than the hospital canteen, where friendly enquiries sometimes probed too deeply. I realise now how good that solitary time was; I could adjust on my own with no one else's grief to care for.

In my room in the evenings I had time to think. It was vital for me to know what I believed about death, and the reality of Christ. I luckily had a little leather New Testament with me, which was a solace. I found my faith unshaken, but when I prayed I felt I was praying to a God a long way away; one who listened but didn't answer.

Quite unexpectedly one day I was told that William was considered well enough to make the journey home; already the hospital had sleepers provisionally booked on the night train the next evening and wanted me to arrange transport from London. I had a brief chat with the consultant who said the disease had been halted. When I asked if we should make plans for a local school he said, 'I don't expect him to live long enough for you to need to worry about that.'

I rang David who arranged to drive up and meet us in London. William, with a great sense of rejoicing, put on his clothes for the first time that afternoon. Next evening he was very impressed to be driven right up to his compartment in an ambulance, and to find the hospital had provided a packed meal for us. The last of their many kindnesses. I felt anxious at being responsible for him on my own. There seemed a great many pills to administer; two were timed for the middle of that night and I had no alarm clock. I had to trust to the jolting of the train and my unease to wake me. Next morning we both looked forward to our reunion with David with great anticipation. It was lovely to see him on the platform. We had a celebratory breakfast in the Station Hotel.

After the bleak austerity of north-east Scotland, Kent looked small and soft and green. At home they were well into spring. The school holidays had just started, four puppies had been born, the daffodils were out. It was all dear, welcoming and familiar, but no longer safe. William went straight to bed delighted to be back in his own room.

So William started a period of convalescence, and to pick up the threads of normal living again, getting up a little more each day. After sitting by the bedside and buying my meals, the cooking, cleaning, washing and ironing of home came in sharp contrast. Momentarily I was surprised how much there was to be done; as my hands worked my mind was on other things. The first day I forgot to get the washing in off the line until the evening; I had to go out into the dark back garden, to where the sheets hung ghostly against the shadows of the trees. I noticed I had a new confidence as I approached the black shapes of the bushes; the protection I had felt in Aberdeen was still with me.

Those first days at home were some of the most difficult. Our doctor advised us to keep the nature of William's illness a secret, both for his own sake and that of the younger children. Looking back I am sure the decision was right for that time, but how it isolated and cut me off. It was like walking about inside a glass box. My friends couldn't see that I was surrounded by an invisible wall. I couldn't talk to them about the one thing that mattered, so our conversation became dull and lifeless, unless somehow it came dangerously close to the forbidden topic. Then it was permeated with a hideous life of its own; after such an encounter I would feel waves of shock gradually dying away through my nervous system. So many ordinary situations had the power to cut me to the heart – and there was no forearming against them. Meal time discussions about plans for the future, memories of the past; the casual enquiry after the children, poignant music, even William's outgrown dufflecoat hanging on a door.

The first time we went out to a meal, I remember a fellow guest asked across the table, "Tell me, what is your eldest boy going to do when he leaves school?" I drew back as if he had offered me a serpent. I could hardly say, 'Go to heaven, I hope,' Nor could I answer enquirers with,'Oh, all the children are well thank you, except my eldest son is dying, but we don't talk about that.' It was the 'not talking about it' that made us feel so cut off and deceitful. The people who shared our secret assumed a great importance to us at that time, but they were very few. I started to suffer some of the physical symptoms of anxiety, without realising what they were. I often felt a constriction at the base of my throat making it difficult to swallow. And when I did swallow, there was the slight nausea one gets in pregnancy. I thought it was rather like pregnancy in reverse –

this giving death – with many of the same symptoms. On getting up I never knew if it would be a good day – or a bad day; a day filled with the lethargy of unshed tears, or a day of energy with plenty to do.

Frustration underlay the fatigue; it must be against the very nature of motherhood to endure such a situation, and do nothing about it. To see a child in mortal danger and take no action, except to wait. I remember the worst time was about seven in the evening. I think it is a low point for many women alone preparing a meal. The reserves of energy were low, and many a quiet tear splashed in among the vegetable peelings.Though I managed a cheerful face by the time the meal was ready and I had company again, the younger children, in their happy oblivion, were a great help. After only three weeks at home, I remember wondering in bed how I could possibly bear another such three. And then – how dared I wish *not* to bear them – when the only escape was the unthinkable disaster which I dreaded for all the family as much as myself.

I had a horror of funerals those first weeks. The words Funeral Director were abhorrent to me. I loathed their arid pavement-side windows with their grey memorial urns. In imagination I dared to walk all the way down the path ahead, until I got to that. How could my children face it, particularly the ten and twelve year old. They did so much with William; his company and affection had been staple to their growing up.

During each day my heart seemed to accumulate a load of sorrow. I was usually the last to go to bed, and could go downstairs to be alone to pray. I remembered 'Come unto me all ye who are heavy laden, and I will refresh you.' I did find refreshment and a certain peace as I prayed, but it was a frail thing, nothing to rely upon. I did not feel abandoned by God, but I don't think I felt Him with me either. I knew I was at the end of my resources and I was blindly feeling for his help. Once David was asleep I often cried. I remember the scalding, silent tears soaking into

14

my pillow many nights. They could flow once everyone was safely asleep.

One night I had gone to bed tired and sad, and slept almost at once. It felt only a few minutes later that I had the most vivid dream. I was standing looking up at a large wooden cross held above and before me. A voice said 'Take up thy cross and follow me.' With great joy I opened my arms for it, and as I did so, it came nearer, getting smaller all the time, until it was just the right size to fit into my heart, where it lodged. I seemed to wake at once feeling alert, happy, full of peace — and went comfortably back to sleep again.

Next morning the dream seemed absolutely real, an actual event, the nicest thing that could have happened.

I had been a Christian for ten years. In the months before William was ill I had been uncomfortable and a little sad, when I came across Christ's clear directive to those who would follow him. I had no cross in my comfortable happy life and I couldn't see or think of anything suitable. I didn't realise that Christ does not want us to carry a cross all the time, that any suffering can be a cross and that we don't choose them for ourselves. Perhaps that was the reason I welcomed that dream cross with such joy. That and the sense that Christ had touched my sorrow, changed it from being a lonely, destructive burden.

In the time I had been a Christian, I had had very little teaching other than what I discovered as I read the New Testament. I thought about the dream very carefully to see how I could follow Christ in carrying my part of the cross. I thought I must carry it with obedience, opting out of as little of my share of the experience as possible. It must be totally accepted and so somehow given back to God. I suddenly felt that to bear a cross for Christ, however, unworthily, was a great privilege. Now the situation had this wholly new dimension, it slipped into a new perspec-

15

tive; my sorrow was mixed with something not unlike joy.

Yet at the same time at the back of my mind I wondered if accepting pain, suffering and death for someone else was not a rather soft option?

3: New school, new heart

Every day now William was getting stronger, his complicated schedule of pills being reduced. No longer did I set the alarm for the small hours to brave our freezing passage with his night time dose. Our family doctor paid carefully casual visits until he was strong enough to be up and about. The doctor suggested that we should ask a local consultant to hold a watching brief on the case. For treatment we decided he should attend the local teaching hospital in Canterbury, which was only twenty miles away, rather than be subjected to frequent trips to the Marsden in London. I was assured that the pathologist in Canterbury would have the benefit of all the latest London research. We were determined that what was left of his life should be as carefree and natural as possible.

William was no longer strong enough to work on the farm as he usually did at home, but became an assiduous co-pilot of the family car instead. As we live in an isolated place it was frequently on the move, and he soon passed his Test. Somehow we got him a second hand Hillman Imp which was a great source of interest and satisfaction and gave him a measure of independence. His old energy seemed to be pouring back, and David and I started to wonder how, with no farm work, he was going to occupy himself.

Our doctor called one day on Helena, our youngest, in bed with a nice ordinary straightforward childish complaint. On his way out, I tried to get some help with how we should plan for William's immediate future. The only advice he could give me, was to be prepared for his final illness to start at any moment. That was not the first time he had emphasised this point. I am sure it was his way of sparing me future shock. He may have sensed the new peace I had since the dream, and feared I was living in a fool's paradise. It wasn't the first time he had said it, but somehow that morning it was a body blow to the heart.

It was shortly after that that we made a family expedition to Sandwich, and picnicked in the spring sunshine on the beach. Leaning against a sandhill watching the children's enjoyment of each other's company, and the cold sea sparkling beyond, the pain in my heart was almost tangible — a knife thrust and twist I had become familiar with. How could I bear to live not knowing if they had days, months or years before the blow fell.

When they went off to shop and explore the ancient streets, I was too sick at heart to keep with them, but turned into St. Peter's to ostensibly to look round, but really for solitude. It was there in that peaceful grey emptiness that God in his love told me what I so needed to know. I cannot think why I should have had this marvellous dispensation. I can only believe that the many prayers for us at the time, some from people who didn't know us, opened a path for this mercy.

The idea came to me a few days later while I was washing the kitchen floor, that we'd better get on with sending William to school. Why not send him to King's School, Canterbury, as a day boy? I could see all sorts of reasons why not, the very first being the difficulty of getting him accepted four days before the start of a new term. The idea had such force, however, I never doubted that this was the plan for us to follow, and that we would be successful. A friend spoke to the headmaster for us, and we went to see him, William waiting in the car outside. He heard our request with sympathy and accepted William into the sixth form at once. Then he asked to meet him. William came in looking large, dependable and very

18

healthy; the words still dying on the air between us seemed grotesque at the sight of his cheerful face. He had approved the plan himself already. The sadness of losing his friends in the north was far outweighed by living at home, and driving himself to school each day in the Imp. He attended a weekly blood clinic in Canterbury anyway, so that would fit in with his work. That soon proved an extra bit of freedom which could release him from the more irksome lessons, or let him off early if he felt tired. He entered into this new school's life with a kind of good humoured detachment. Being such an old foundation, all sorts of school customs and traditions had grown up which were in sharp contrast with the school he had been used to. They were inclined to tickle his sense of humour, but he was as broad minded as he could be about them – only saving them up to recount at home. He enjoyed it all thoroughly and started to make a lot of friends. If there was any strain it didn't show. Being excused games he was able to get home early most days. It was such a pleasure to see that slightly rakish blue Imp come bumping triumphantly into the farm yard. He grew to know all possible routes home through the lanes, and the beautiful isolated stretch of country running along the top of the North Downs. I think he was happy at that time; he was soon well enough to be allowed to swim and play a little leisurely tennis. I remember he even played in a cricket match against the fathers. Watching his lean, sunburnt figure bowling, I couldn't believe his illness had affected his game as badly as that; afterwards he explained he was bowling badly on purpose, they were giving the fathers a chance! I didn't enjoy those summer functions much. Luckily we weren't known to many of the staff; it was a drain of emotional and nervous energy having to discuss post-'A' level plans with teachers who didn't know how little post-'A' level there might be.

So a new routine grew up and a thin layer of normality spread over our daily lives. The house was empty all day until the school bus left Helena at the top of our lane. Or the Hillman Imp returned. Those empty days gave my imagination too free a rein. I had to keep my mind occupied. I found quite early that self pity was destructive, something to avoid at all costs. In fact I had an experience which left me determined not to give in to it.

Alone one afternoon I started feeling very sorry for myself, and decided to go to my bedroom for a 'good cry'. I threw myself on my bed and buried my face in the pillow when I had the strongest sense of not being alone. There was a sympathetic presence standing by the bed, rather in the way a nurse would attend a patient, just observing and waiting for the bout to be over. I couldn't go on crying like that, for myself. I felt too self-conscious under that patient observation. I got up and went downstairs again. I think of that experience when I read of the crowd of witnesses with which St. Paul says we are surrounded. After that I didn't care to give in to self pity; it was a very useful lesson. But it was hard not expressing the grief and anguish I felt stifled within. There was no place for it at medical consultations or in talking to the few people who shared our secret. I did not want to add it to David's burden. I remember once I chanced to hear an operatic soprano on the radio, pouring out all her anguish in song. It is not a thing that I ordinarily enjoy, but I revelled in the sound; it was as if the song in my heart was expressed. It gave me extraordinary relief to listen to her, and to relate not only to her grief but to her sense of outrage. I too was outraged at the tragic fate that was overtaking my child. Illogically outraged at the apparent detachment, and calm of the doctors and specialists; anguished and outraged, and it all had to be buried. Gradually I learnt to share these feelings with the Lord, to pour them out to him, like everything else I talked to him about my heart. Not that he didn't know all of it already, and in exchange he gave me a little of his peace.

So life went on. I went back to my afternoon at the

Citizens Advice Bureau, which I had given up when William was first ill. One day the citizens wisely kept their problems to themselves, and without them my own seemed to press in on me. I read the report book, and tried to memorise some of the new legislation, but my mind felt stifled. I prayed as usual, but the feeling persisted. I desperately needed to discuss my own situation, or find out more about it, but nobody wanted to talk, least of all the doctors. There was no one to talk to, no book, no film, no T.V. or radio programme for my problem. I seemed enmeshed in a conspiracy of silence. On the way home I went in to the public library, and glanced listlessly round the shelves, though I was sure no book would deal with my burning preoccupation. As I came out I passed the Religious Section and one title stood out catching my eye: 'Thy Son Liveth'. I took the book down and opened it; suddenly the silence was broken. This book, written by a priest, the father of a young man with cancer, spoke straight to my heart. At last here was some one faced with our problem, discussing it in all its implications, medical physical and spiritual. It is a fascinating and moving book, now sadly out of print. I read it all that evening and felt immense relief and inspiration. Here was someone recounting his own grief, and God's answers to prayer for his son. He spoke of a God who was willing to intervene. He spoke of the healing power of Christ released through the laying on of christian hands. Until then I had heard nothing of this ministry. What I read now of this man's fight to save his son, opened up entirely new vistas. I felt encouraged, and determined to nurse William at home myself when his illness came. The book also led us, by a series of tenuous links, to the place that was to help us so much in the coming months.

One sunny June afternoon some weeks later, I was weeding the flower bed by our front door when the postman arrived and handed me a letter from David's sister in Devonshire. We had only recently told her the nature of William's disease: she was too close to the family not to realise something drastic was wrong, otherwise we would not have told her at all. Years before she had lost a small daughter herself, with the same illness; we didn't want to revive sad memories.

Brushing the earth off my hands to open her letter, I had no premonition of the appalling news it would contain. Unbelievingly I read that, having heard from us, she had grown suspicious of her eldest daughter, Jane's lethargy and insisted on her having a blood test. This was exactly the reaction we had feared and tried to delay, but in our worst moments we had never foreseen that the test would prove positive.

My heart felt ready to break for my sister in law. I couldn't bear to think of her feeling all that I had felt in the last months. Now that our two families faced an identical tragedy, the situation had a new nightmarish quality which immensely increased its menacing power. How could our children survive experiencing the sickness, and the death, of these two, whose lives were so closely linked to their own? Especially I feared for Angela, just nineteen, the nearest in age to William and his very good friend. She had spent her previous summer holiday on her own with Jane, camping and touring Scotland. How could she, or indeed my younger two, Jane's cousins, get through without being emotionally destroyed?

The next few days passed in a daze. The normal rules of existence seemed to recede and I was adrift in a lunatic universe where no holds were barred; there were no limits now. One night I dreamt I had lost Helena. After a long and anxious search I found myself looking into the open doors of some rooms in a hospital. Several inert white sheeted figures lay there. I tiptoed forward and found that one was William. A nurse appeared and pointed to a small figure in the neighbouring cubicle, connected by many tubes to some kind of machine. 'That's Helena', she said, 'You will find Angela further down the corridor. They are injecting her half hourly — the other two have been taken upstairs.

A couple of days later I was due to judge Shetland sheepdogs at Ardingly, the South of England Agricultural Show. I couldn't cancel the engagement so David suggested driving me there. One of the ring side spectators was a young mother with a child on her lap. I remember glancing at her and the bitter thought that crossed my mind — that the child she so innocently held was in truth a kind of time bomb, primed to go off some time in its future, possibly to devastate her life for ever.

With a kind of bitter determination and a growing sense of unreality, I completed the judging and then we started for home. On the way back, quite unusually for David, we got lost, and eventually found ourselves in the village of Groombridge. As I saw the village sign I suddenly remembered it from 'My Son Liveth', This was the place where Dorothy Kerin had spent the last years of her ministry of healing. This was where Burrswood, which had been such a source of encouragement and help to Frank Drake, the author of 'Thy Son Liveth', had been founded. I knew that Dorothy Kerin had died some years before and thought that Burrswood had died with her. We went into the churchyard to look for her grave, and found it, small and unpretentious, among many others. As we came out we saw the gates of Burrswood across the village green, with a notice announcing it as 'The Dorothy Kerin Trust'.

So Burrswood still existed. I rang the next day hoping they might have a copy of 'Thy Son Liveth' which was out of print and unobtainable in book shops. I hoped that it might help my sister in law, as it had helped me. Burrswood could not supply a copy of the book either, but the person to whom I spoke suggested I might attend a service of healing, as a proxy for William and Jane. Until that moment I had no idea that there were such things as Services of Healing. The New Testament is full of accounts of healings taking place in the name of Christ.

But I imagined these had stopped a few hundred years later. Healing was something I vaguely associated with saints and cranks, but saints were now in short supply.

I decided to go, and drove over the following Thursday morning, very tense, very shy, very desperate. I found the gates we had seen the previous weekend, drove up the long wooded drive to the main house and parked outside. There were a lot of other parked cars, and the chapel, when I found it, was full. The service had started. I remember standing in the aisle waiting my turn to go up to the altar with tears pouring down my face. I wasn't only there for William and Jane but for all the lives bound up with theirs. It needed a miracle at least, a double miracle, and the more I thought about it, the more I wept. I felt nothing during the laying on of the priest's hands. After the service I slipped away as quickly as I could.

The next day I was preparing for a full house that coming weekend but though my hands worked, my mind would not get involved; it reverted to my fear of the future. By the time William got back from school, apparantly healthy, happy and full of chat, I was far into mourning for him, and had to adjust with a jolt as we drank tea together over the kitchen table. It was difficult to equate this big, sunburnt son of mine with all that I dreaded. I know I was tired by the end of the day, and approached my prayers despondently. At that time I used to use some words from Thomas A Kempis' *Imitation of Christ*, from the section called 'The Highway of the Holy Cross'. As I was saying them that evening I suddenly felt my whole body filled with light and that light came from God; in a mysterious way, was God. Every cell of my body felt penetrated by it, and I knew that God had taken possession of every smallest part of me. I remember looking at my wrist lying on the bed by which I knelt and thinking how each tiny cell of the skin was full of this invisible light. I do not know how long the sensation lasted; I certainly cannot describe it. The next day, and

24

every day since has been different.

Many writers have referred to such an experience. St. Paul called it 'Putting on the new man'. In the Old Testament Ezekiel tells us of God's promise to give his people 'new hearts and a new spirit, to take from them their hearts of stone and give them tender hearts of love for God' (Ezekiel 11 v. 19, Living Bible). It seemed that something very like that had happened to me. With it came a great thirst and desire for God, not just for his help but for himself. Suddenly I could face the future. My new heart trusted God and Christ. The sting had gone out of the situation and with it all bitterness and fear. As a gift of love I had received the pearl of great price for which the world is well lost, and I realised that nothing could take us from the hand that gave it. To me it was God's answer to my desperate cry at the service the previous day. He had healed my heart.

4: University

When the summer holidays came William decided he wanted to drive up to Scotland to stay with two of his old school friends, who were living in a caravan. It sounded great fun, but I wondered whether he could be away from the blood clinic for so long. I didn't relish his being so far from home either. But he managed to beg off one of his weekly blood tests, giving himself two weeks' freedom. Then we discovered that the father of one of his friends was a doctor, so we were able to send his medical details ahead, just in case.

We had friends who offered to lend us a flat near Keswick so we went there with Jamie and Helena to have a holiday at the same time. We wanted to be alone with them; so much of our time at home was taken up by work, and there was always the distracting undertow of William's illness. Also David was teaching full time at a neighbouring secondary school during the term, so that in the school holidays there was a great deal of farm work crying out to be done, and not much time for the children, unless they were involved in it too.

William spent the first couple of nights with us and then set off for Scotland in his Hillman Imp. It looked a frail bark to be setting off on such a journey. I remember the pleasure and relief with which I saw it bumping triumphantly back into our farm yard a couple of weeks later. William was a little bit in love, and in very good spirits. His clothes were all in great need of a wash, and his canvas shoes so bad that by common consent we threw them away.

If I hadn't learnt a little bit about meditation and prayer

by that time, I don't think I could have endured the separation as peacefully as I did. In the course of the year a few people had to be told about his illness, people who saw a lot of him had to know for his own safety. They sometimes said 'I don't know how you can live like this. We never guessed there was anything wrong.' In fact I had learnt a source of strength, which was renewed from day to day. Each day I tried to find an uninterrupted hour for reading, thinking and praying. It is surprising how contrary to human nature this procedure seems to be. Contrary to my nature anyway! As the allotted time drew near I was always tempted to postpone it, all sorts of practical tasks would clamour for attention. Tasks that I was happy to leave undone in the morning became strangely attractive and important as the hour approached. When finally I settled down, I often felt rather a fool, but oh how that hour paid off in dividends of real strength and peace. I usually read the New Testament until I found a piece that caught my attention particularly; then I thought about it till I wanted to pray. Sometimes I took an idea and tried to concentrate on it until my mind was undistracted, and I felt drawn to God. So I took time each day to try and approach Him, and when I did that I found I was rested, strengthened, given an awareness of beauty and the capacity to enjoy life, in spite of everything. In those days it seemed to be a matter of emptying my mind enough to let Christ in. The smallest achievement had great results. I realise now how fortunate it was that I hadn't a strong enough personality to manage on my own. By nature I wouldn't have taken that time for prayer if I could have managed without it, but luckily I couldn't; little by little I started to discover some lovely things that I never would have known.

During that last school year William's blood count, except for a few minor fluctuations, remained steady, his strength continued to improve. He was able to drive the tractor again, and feed the calves at weekends. He bought an old motor bike which he and a friend worked on, intending to get it back on the road. It was good for scrambling in the fields but fortunately was never reliable enough to wean him away from the Imp as transport. Nevertheless he managed a fall from the pillion of his friend's bike. We were rung late one night to hear that he was in hospital with cuts on his head. They kept him in over night for observation and we collected him next morning, his scalp neatly stitched. They hadn't checked his wallet when he was brought in, so they missed the card warning them he was on steroids. Fortunately his blood clotted well so it wasn't relevant.

I don't think he missed the sports and athletics he had been so good at; the freedom he had to drive home when the others played games more than compensated him and he used it to the full, often dropping in at the homes of friends. His social life increased enormously and there were plenty of parties. He would creep with humorous, exaggerated care into our bedroom last thing at night, determined to share the evening's doing with us, if we weren't asleep; sometimes we very nearly were, but hadn't the heart to keep our eyes closed and miss that last half hour's chat as he sat on the bottom of our bed. He was very good at sharing the small triumphs and disasters of farm and garden, and took an affectionate interest in all of Helena's twelve-year-old doings. She was just out of rabbits and into guinea pigs at the time. He shared with us the traumatic catastrophic morning when Andrew, Jamie's beautiful cream coloured ferret, escaped for the second time running, butchering all of Helena's guinea pigs that had escaped him before. David shot him on sight; he wanted it done before Jamie was awake. Only he was awake already, and heard the shot. The mourning in Rama had nothing on our house for the next couple of hours.

We did wonder whether we should tell William that he had leukaemia, but it seemed a grotesque thing to do, when he was leading a happy normal life. I had told him that he had a rare blood disease for which there was no known cure, but I had added that I hoped he would grow out of it, or a cure be found. I am glad we spared him from carrying the burden of this knowledge all through the time he was well, but we should have told him during his final illness, it would have absolved him from fighting the disease in the way he did. I am sorry I didn't trust William to Christ enough then, enough to take him through the experience of suffering pain without any hope of relief except death. While he was well we prayed that Christ would protect his mind from the knowledge of his disease. It seemed a lot to ask. As one of our doctor's junior partners said, 'You can't tell me an intelligent boy like that, studying Biology, Physics and Chemistry at 'A' level, and having weekly blood checks, hasn't guessed what is wrong with him.' But he hadn't, and didn't. It was something I had prayed about. We had decided to tell him if he asked, and I trusted I should be given the right words when the time came. Many a time my heart missed a beat expecting that question. If ever he was inexplicably very late back from school, I used to fear that he had discovered it on his own. In my mind's eye I saw his car parked in some country lane with him in it, perhaps weeping, alone. But his mind seemed to be marvellously protected – as was confirmed when we read his journal for the first time. Gradually I grew to rely on this protection. I remember once him telling me about a Biology lesson he had enjoyed. It had been on the structure of the blood, and digressed to cover the effect of cancer on the blood cells. As he explained it all to me, I felt my own blood chill, but still his protection held.

If we could have managed in any other way except this way of trusting Christ's love and care for us, I am afraid we would have taken it, thinking it more reliable and practical because we had a hand in it ourselves. If I could have given William a pill that would have protected his mind be sure I would have done so, but as it was against our very nature, we learnt that there is nothing more reliable and practical than trusting in Christ. He is especially close to the suffering and the broken hearted. It's a lesson I am still learning in other people's lives, it seems to have no limit.

As the summer term approached it was time to plan the next phase for William. Among his friends University applications were flying here and there, probable grades were being exhaustively canvassed, all were full of future plans. He had applied to two universities, Leeds and London, the latter for an agricultural degree course at Wye College, near our home. I prayed that, if he was going to University, he would be accepted by, and choose Wye. Though the doctors reassured me that it would be as good for William to go to Leeds — that the medical care could be as good there — I was not persuaded about that. He left at dawn to get to Leeds by train in time for his interview. When he got back late that night he told us it had been only just light on his way to the station and he had had the extraordinary experience of nearly hitting a small deer, which was mysteriously crossing the road. Leeds, when he got there, had impressed him very much, but later Wye attracted him even more. I was thankful for that; it seemed a sensible decision of his to remain near his friends and the doctors he trusted.

At last came the final term at school, with all the normal festivities and end of term formalities, for which we had to put on our best clothes and attend, thankfully, for the last time.

I watched William drive off to take his 'A' levels. Neither he nor I had much confidence in their outcome, he had missed so much. Providentially in the event there were enough questions on the work he had done, and he got good grades. Both universities had places for him. I went to see the Bursar at Wye and told him the situation. We felt it was only fair the College should know that they were giving the place to a student with such little expectation of life. We shall always be grateful to Wye for taking him; it gave him a continued purpose within easy reach of home, friends and the doctors he was soon bound to need.

The College reduced the usual entry requirement of a year's practical work, to two months, in view of his medical history, though the reason given was that he lived on a farm. As harvest was approaching it wasn't hard to find a farm that needed an extra hand for a couple of months. If we had had the chance we should have tried to get him a place on a non-arable farm, dairying perhaps; where he could have got experience while avoiding the crises and work pressures of harvest. But almost at once he had fixed himself up on an arable farm we didn't know, near one of his school friends. So we watched him revel in the work, coming home late each evening, huge, dusty and happy, putting in far more overtime and energy than was good for him. I found a crumpled bit of paper on the table by his bed on which he kept a nightly record of his hours and the wages due. I realized then that the combination of work that he loved, his first real earnings, and the challenge to his powers of endurance, were powerful and potentially dangerous, but without seeming over anxious and interfering there was very little I could do. I tried ringing up the farmer who employed him, but got an unsympathetic hearing, and the hours continued to pile up.

Before two months were up, the hip pain which had heralded the onset of the disease the previous year, was back, and his steroid intake had to be increased. A couple of weeks later he came back from a blood check and casually mentioned that the pills he was on weren't working any longer, so the specialist would be changing his treatment. I did something then for which I have been thankful. I picked up my tiny camera from the hall table, and stepping outside took two shots of him standing in the sun where he had got out of his car. I realised that except for the slight fullness in his cheeks, as a result of the steroids, this might be one of the last occasions I should

31

see him looking himself, and we had only one other photograph taken since he was ill. I had to continue by taking a couple of the beloved car.

We went to the next blood check together, as we often had. How familiar I was with the rather dingy hospital corridor which served as our waiting room. Before we left the pathologist asked to speak to me. Full of foreboding I suggested to William that perhaps he had hung about long enough, and would be better joining Helena who was waiting in the car park. As I waited to be summoned, on one of a row of canvas and metal tubular chairs, I was reminded in a sickening way of the times I had waited to see one or other of the family's headmasters, but this time I was dreadfully frightened of what I was going to be told. I prayed hard as I followed the nurse down the corridor.

It struck me as strange at the time, and it still does, that there can be an interview like the one that followed in the pathologist's tiny, glass sided office. He and an Asian houseman were there. I think if the pathologist had any idea how I was feeling, he might have treated me differently, but possibly he feared he had some tough nut to deal with, a religious crank perhaps, who might stand between her son and and the treatment he wanted to give. It is true he had been told that we didn't believe in prolonging William's life, unless it was worth living. I was still haunted by the idea of him dragging out his days helpless in some hospital. Maybe that accounted for the clinical detachment with which the interview was handled. He started by saying that he was going to be quite honest with me. Until that moment it had never occurred to me that he would consider being anything else. We were now at a point of decision, he said, either to stop treating William and let the illness have its way, or to embark upon a periodic course of injections. These were strong and would have to be given in hospital. There was also the risk of side effects; if we were unlucky they could cause brain damage. They would anyway cause total baldness, but he should feel well between treatments, and when the time came he would have a quick and easy death. The alternative, which he did not favour, would mean a gradual decline, followed by a slower, more painful death. So that sunny afternoon in Canterbury, in the little glass sided office, I was asked to weigh the advantages of a quick and easy death, carrying the risk of William's mind being affected, against the slow and painful death, without that risk. I chose the first alternative. The Pathologist was satisfied it was the right decision. I left the room sickened. If I had been a blood donor I would have been offered a cup of tea, possibly somewhere to recover for a few minutes. I had only agreed to a quick and easy death for my son, carrying the risk of brain damage, and the certainty of baldness, so there wasn't even a tubular chair for me.

In a few seconds I was outside walking through the warm sunlight to where Helena and William waited in the car, both equally impatient. They wanted to know what on earth I had been doing. When we got home I locked myself into the first place, the lavatory, and rested my forehead against the wall. I had come to the end of my resources; there was nothing left to go on with. I would never make another decision; as a person I was finished. I wasn't even able to unlock the door. From this utter need I prayed to Christ for help – it was my only hope. I don't know quite what happened, but a few minutes later I was in the kitchen getting the tea.

Soon the unaccustomed riches from William's farm work were burning a hole in his pocket. He decided to spend a couple of nights with Liz in London to buy himself some new clothes. Everything that wasn't school uniform seemed to have perished on the farm. He had only been away a night and half a day when Liz rang me to say that he had bad pains in his back, and she didn't think he was well enough to be away from home. I met him off the next train, wearing the only shirt he had time to buy. As he turned away I saw the back was soaked with sweat. He ached and sweated through the next three weeks; his hair, thick on the pillow each morning, had to be collected and thrown away. His mouth was so ulcerated he could only swallow liquidised foods. We imagined the illness had returned, but after examining him in hospital the pathologist told us that it was an allergic reaction to an injection he had been given. Perhaps they had tried a preliminary dose before our conversation in his office; there were no more injections after that. It took him three unpleasant weeks to recover, and at the end he was totally bald.

5: Illness

The time at Wye College was a great success. William enjoyed it from the moment he got there, late and without hair as he was. The work interested him, and soon he was deeply involved in the social scene, including some memorable parties and a hilarious appearance in the First Year Review: as 'Gari Baldi, the Galloping Gourmet' he gave a demonstration of Italian cuisine, involving yards of uncontrollable cooked spaghetti and a good deal of audience participation. His car often came rattling down our hill full of friends, so we were kept in touch with the news. The house was exactly the right distance away, not too close to be an unwelcome influence but easy to reach when he felt like it. At the end of term a small bill arrived from the Bursar for William's share in the damage caused at an inter-term water battle. Not a thing to gladden the hearts of most parents, but we settled ours with pleasure.

Not far from where we lived there was a geriatric hospital. With William away I had a little time to spare, so spent some there as a tray carrier and washer-upper. I soon saw that there was much more than that that I could do for the very necessitous patients, and started to think about training as an S.E.N. But the hours and times wouldn't fit. That was perhaps why I offered myself, when I heard that Burrswood were looking for an auxillary nurse. The Sister in Charge reckoned she could give me enough training, so I started for two days a week. The skill and loving service given to each patient was a revelation to me; nothing that could be done was too much trouble. The whole place had an atmosphere of love which, I noticed, I consciously missed when I was about outside. The patients were mostly people facing exceptional problems, progressive disabling disease, terminal illness, or some other emotionally or physically disabling trauma. They were sustained with skill, love and prayer, and allowed to die with the maximum human dignity, if that came while they were in the Nursing Home. I was strengthened in my new found belief that death was not something to be frightened of but a forward step, a birth into all that came next, and sometimes an opportunity for those companioning the dying, to be very near to God. I prayed that William should die at home and that we should be together when his time came.

But life wasn't all nursing, or thinking about William. There were plenty of other things to do, the Christmas shopping for instance. December was slipping by leaving not quite enough time or money to get that done in comfort — a very normal characteristic. We decided to have one of David's non-teaching days in London together, and get as much done as we could. We drove up and were soon questing through the Oxford Street shops for presents and the other things on our list. At mid-day we met to eat and compare notes; we were doing well, the list was dwindling. We set out together for Heal's. As we walked up the Tottenhan Court Road I met a girl who embodied all my worst fears. She was the spectre who had haunted my subconscious from the beginning, the one who made me beg that they should not prolong William's life to be an invalid, the one who gained credibility with the Pathologist's talk of a 'long slow decline'. She might have materialised out of the pavement in front of me. A wraith-like red haired girl, paper-white, paper-thin, just strong enough to walk, one emaciated wrist on the arm of a nurse. Her clothes hung; the person who dressed her had set her pathetically gay beret at just the wrong angle. I stood stock still, aghast. Dear God, not this — not this for us. Then she had passed. I do hope she hadn't seen my confusion, there were plenty of other people on the pavement and David obviously hadn't seen her. I didn't mention her either; I spared him the more tortured labyrinths of my mind when I could.

William's first serious illness, since the onset of the disease in Scotland, started at the College dance. A nagging pain in his hip increased during the evening, until it drove him first to bed, then to the sick bay. The following morning we had a phone call to say he was driving himself home. By the time he reached us he could scarcely walk; we both had to help him to bed. After three days he went back to hospital in an ambulance. As we watched it departing up the lane, I knew that everyone in the know, including our doctor, thought he was dying; they didn't expect us to see him come back. Those not in the know, in the village, and in the family, were saddened to see the ambulance and realised the illness must be taken seriously. We rang Burrswood, and our praying friends, to alert them to William's urgent need.

The best part of each of the following days I spent with him in hospital. It was very like our time in Aberdeen over again, only now I sensed he was sicker than before. In the afternoons when he slept, I wandered into Canterbury, a town I did not know well at that time. I needed two things; something to eat, somewhere to pray – the time to pray most, the time to come closer to God and be comforted. It was easy finding something to eat, but finding somewhere to pray was more difficult. I tried the Cathedral first, but even in December it was full of visitors, tourists and their voices. Taking the steps down to the beautiful chapel in the crypt, I found a lovely tranquil place, but in a few minutes two elderly ladies with bags of fish and chips settled on the row of chairs behind me. They had come for a comfortable chat with their meal – one of the pleasures of their outing. I couldn't blame them, but nor could I pray. In those days there didn't seem a single refuge of quiet in that cathedral. Part of other lunch hours I spent sitting in the car park opposite the

United Reformed Church. Through the windscreen I could see the great wooden cross on the church wall, that made a quieter, more private place, and the cross reminded me of the one in my dream.

It was a sad time; I didn't really believe William was dying at only nineteen, but it looked like it and somehow the hospital separated me from him. I didn't know what he was thinking. Then gradually, in spite of all forebodings, the fever started to subside. To our delight we were allowed to fetch him home a few days before Christmas. What a joyful homecoming that was, and how good to see him having a cup of tea in the kitchen once more before we helped him to bed. But our joy was soon dashed; perhaps the journey had been too much for him. The remission ended and for three days before Christmas he was only conscious in snatches.

Nevertheless rather subdued preparations for Christmas continued in the rest of the house. We knew that the least detail of normal family living was vital for our beloved younger children. In the months ahead we were both to be stretched on this crux of our situation, how to provide simultaneously a good home to die in and to grow up in.

Filling the stockings on Christmas Eve, William's was filled as a poignant formality. But at five o'clock on Christmas morning he woke clear headed, and asked straight away where it was. Later in the day, while Christmas followed its course downstairs, he even felt well enough to eat some turkey. Could it be that the prayers of so many friends at Midnight Mass had achieved this small miracle? It was a great blessing and help for us all over Christmas. Next day the dispensation was over and acute illness returned to stay for many weeks.

The onset of the illness was violent. Almost at once he was too ill to be moved to hospital. At home he had every care our love could devise, except we couldn't inject the morphine he soon needed. We had to call the doctor at all hours of the day and night for that. Soon the delay became intolerable, so it was decided that David should be allowed to give injections; after all, he had years of practice on the sheep!

None of us really remember how long that illness went on. For week after agonised week William lay at the mercy of an unpredictable sea of pain, sometimes so rough it swamped his very consciousness, at others lapping round him as it searched out new areas to exploit. It was too deepseated to be wholly dispelled by morphine even combined with other drugs; the timetable for these had to be strictly adhered to. Waiting between injections while the effect of one wore off, and it was still too early to give another, reminded me of the last stages of childbirth, so total and all enveloping was the pain. With it came a high fever which could saturate three pairs of sheets in a day.

David's school gave him compassionate leave because William was so gravely ill. The years he had spent in hospitals with a leg wound gave him an invaluable insight into nursing, and we needed every bit. We had been thrown in at the deep end, but both of us had a strangely cheerful feeling of calm and confidence. We had discovered that Christ's saying 'My grace is sufficient for you' is to be taken literally; it was true, real, absolutely dependable.

It wasn't long before David had to show me how to give injections, so that he could sometimes leave the house or get some precious sleep. Without grace, that was something I never could have done, I who feared injections from childhood, and even found the routine immunisation of the children mildly traumatic. Nor could I have witnessed William's suffering, but through it all the inner peace held. I was able to be with him, sometimes to hold him in my arms, and pray through the pain and then leave him if he slept and join the normal life downstairs. We had his room wired for sound to make this possible.

The days and nights were divided between us. Sometimes we took half a night each, it seemed easier to catch up on sleep that way; struggling awake with the

39

alarm in the small hours, into some clothes, then down the freezing silent passage to where the light showed under William's door. Inside it would be warm, and still, disturbed only by the gentle hum of the electric Ripple bed, or on a bad night noises from the bed itself. We were glad when College term started shortly after his illness, though I sorely missed Angela's help and company. It must have been hard for her sleeping in the next room, the adjoining wall was so thin. We kept records of all the pills and injections, with notes on William's condition; they helped at the night time take-over and were useful for the doctor too.

The three doctors from our local practice were wonderfully good to us; one I particularly remember stripping to his shirt sleeves in the early hours of one morning and helping to change the saturated sheets, another time to move the heavy bed out from the wall, so that we could get to either side.

One evening the Consultant came and he, with the two doctors, examined William thoroughly. The unaccustomed movement of his limbs was very painful. I went downstairs and waited until they joined us by the drawing room fire. Glancing away from the Consultant as he spoke, my eyes rested on the familiar room. How could it all look so much the same, as the background to such a conversation? He explained that internal bleeding from William's bones was forcing apart the membrane which sheathed them, this was the cause of the pain. He did not believe he could survive more than another two weeks, indeed, if his heart had not been young and strong, the pain might have killed him already. There was nothing we could do that wasn't being done, except that now we could increase the amount of morphine he was allowed. There was no longer any reason to prevent his becoming addicted.

News came from the hospital after the next blood check: William could not live more than a few days, unless he was given a massive blood transfusion, and even that would only last a week or so. We felt he had suffered enough and rejected the idea for his sake.

I was still doubtful of the outcome in spite of all the medical evidence. Part of me was open for William to die then, just as I was told, but part remembered the revelation at Sandwich and wondered what was going to happen. It was at one such time of perplexity, when I was praying, that I did something I had never regarded as valid. After praying for guidance, I opened the New Testament which was lying on the bed, and read the first passage my eyes lit upon. I found myself reading Christ's words about Lazarus: 'This illness will not end in death . . .'

We were chatting together in the bathroom a few nights later, getting ready for bed, when we discovered we both noticed an almost imperceptable difference in William; we believed he was getting better. The next day I was able to give him some egg yolk beaten with sugar, the first nourishment for days. The tide of his illness was on the turn.

During the next weeks we watched him struggle back to conscious life, as the pain and fever started to subside, drifting in and out of a more comfortable sleep, taking nourishment from an old-fashioned feeding cup he nicknamed Flook on account of the handle ears and curved trunk-like spout. We saw him smile again at our attempts to make him comfortable. He was marvellously forgetful between bouts of the pain he had suffered, and the bouts were getting further apart and less intense. His need for morphine was less urgent, the waiting time between injections no longer so agonising for him, and us.

We came close to each other during that time, we three who were inter-dependent as we fought the pain and weakness. Chatting and often laughing quietly together in the night, we got to know each other well. We talked about everything under the sun, except religion. He and I had not talked much about that since the start of the illness. I was shy of bringing up a subject he might connect with the possibility of death, although of course he knew how I felt. By this time he was being prayed for by at least three churches as well as our home church in the village. At Burrswood a proxy received the laying on of hands for him at the healing services.

One day when we were alone together he told me that he believed in Christ, and what a struggle he had had thinking it out for himself. 'You know those books you left lying about hoping I might read one. I did, the Screwtape letters really started me thinking.' I think it was my natural untidyness he had been wary of, but I rejoiced at his news.

In two days he brought the subject up again. 'You see I want to give myself to God, all of me, not just my spirit, but my body as well.' I was sure a prayer would take care of that, but he insisted it should be done properly, he didn't want any mistakes. He asked me if my cousin John, the vicar of Highbury, might come down for the night to see him and get it fixed up.

I was sure John would come if he could. He had been a rock to me in the various crises of my life. When he was a curate at All Souls, Langham Place, he had nearly died himself from a virus which had attacked his brain. He had suffered enough to understand all about invalids. I remembered him in the Middlesex with a head as short of hair as William's was now.

John was summoned from London, and out of the kindness of his heart was with us the next day. He and Sally had been praying for William from the start, so our message came as no surprise. Judging by the laughter that issued from the sickroom at the end of their talk, it had been a success. Later that day one of the bad pains started in William's hip. He asked for John, who went in and prayed with him, laying his hands on the pain and rebuking it and the sickness in the name of Christ. We had

42

not heard that kind of prayer before. The pain did not stop at once, but later, when I tentatively asked William how he felt about that prayer, he said that though it hadn't stopped, the pain had died away far short of its normal horrible crescendo, and he had thanked God.

That night he postponed his morphine injection, to be clear headed for the transaction he wanted to make. When I went back to his room later he was radiantly satisfied. He said it had been much easier than he expected; he was obviously confident in what he had done.

It was David's turn to take the second half of the nursing that night. To start with William had been restless, often moaning, but in the small hours he fell into a peaceful sleep. Towards dawn he woke and murmured, 'Would you read to me please, Pa?' David asked what he would like. 'The first epistle to the Thessalonians, the last verse', was the surprising reply. He found it, and read the words 'The grace and the peace of the Lord Jesus Christ be with you.' A moment later William slept again.

The next morning, when we asked him how he knew where to find the quotation, he denied all knowledge of Thessalonians, saying that as far as he knew he had never read the epistle in his life, he wasn't sure that he even could have recalled that it existed. What more clear and loving answer could he have had to his gift of himself the evening before?

From that day we watched a new side of William develop, a side that was totally fascinated by God; it was as if he had been given a lovely new hobby which shone through all his other interests. He was still not strong enough to read for long to himself so we shared what he read. The old vein of light thrillers had palled and we found ourselves searching for good spiritual books, which wasn't easy, tied to a house in the country and with not much experience to go on. He could manage to read the Bible on his own and asked for set readings. Some of the Old Testament delighted him. From that period came his generic name 'ephod' for the short night shirts, which we had slit up the back to lift on and off in his illness. They reminded him of the garment that so scandalised Michal, when David danced for joy before the Lord.

After trial and error Trollope replaced the thriller writers and proved invaluable bedside reading. We started on the political novels. With a little judicious skipping Phineas Finn's precarious rise to affluence and respectability kept us happily enthralled.

William took Communion at least once a week. We found that for him it was a physical restorative as well as a spiritual lifeline. The first service in his room was just after Christmas, when he was barely conscious. The Vicar had been concerned for him from the start of the illness, and suggested we should ring if he showed signs of coming round and would like Communion that Christmas. He was there within minutes of our call to find William propped and ready. How vivid the memory of those beautiful short bedside services remains; the silence in the room as the vicar made his preparations, the comforting sight of him putting on his starched surplice and spreading the white cloth; and William often lying gaunt and still, his face rather yellow, his eyes clouded with sleep or pain, perhaps looking towards the cross on the little table. Many times the change in him afterwards was wonderful, to see his eyes alive again, both colour and peace in his face.

One of the things we learnt during those long hard weeks was a way of praying with William when he was in pain. We had heard John's prayer claiming the power of the cross to rebuke the pain and overcome the sickness. We found that holding him in our arms, sometimes one each side, and praying for him in this way through the crises was an invaluable addition to our armoury of pain killers and became something William looked for at his worst times. At other times the habit grew on me of praying when my hands were on him for any length of time. When I was washing him or rubbing his back, for

44

instance, if he didn't feel like talking I could pray. I gradually learnt my body could be used to bring comfort, the lessening of pain, perhaps healing to his.

Instead of dying as expected, he slowly recovered his strength without any treatment; his blood count improved week by week. Gradually the pain decreased until it could be controlled without injections. Although he had been on the maximum dose of morphine for months, and that had been increased when death was imminent, he had no trouble from withdrawal symptoms. There was one evening when he felt a vague all over unease, but that was cured by a drink of hot milk, whisky and sugar.

David felt he must go back to work as soon as he could, and after a little anxious deliberation William and I decided we could just manage on our own. The problem that exercised our minds was whether I would have the strength and dexterity to get him out of bed onto the commode, should that be necessary, but between us we surmounted that challenge with flying colours. Getting out of bed was a great step forward which he would have been sad to lose.

Soon he was strong enough to get himself into a chair while I made the bed. Then came the great day when the chair was placed by the window in the passage outside, and he made his shaky, wavering way the few yards to it. Before him lay the view he was so often to mention in his journal, the gentle slope of the fields merging into the woods and hills of the weald of Kent; it was glorious that afternoon in the April sunlight. The last time he had seen it, it had been in the grip of a hard December frost.

6: A miracle for a time

Slowly and surely, with no treatment to speak of, his convalescence continued and developed a routine and way of life of its own. After the family left in the mornings, we started our mutual day with the usual sickroom chores and, for me, the rest of the house. But in the afternoons we read aloud until it was my time to walk up the hill to meet Helena on her way back from the school bus. As we sat reading Trollope in the sun one afternoon I felt we had developed the life style of an elderly married couple. It was true we had grown very close to each other, but I thanked God one half of the couple was getting younger and stronger each day. Climbing the stairs for him was less like an assault on Everest, and once up he was no longer marooned, unable to climb down without a long rest.

Talking to William then I noticed he had no recollection of the appalling pains he had suffered, they might never have been. God had healed his memory, as well as his body, and any addiction he might have had. There was no craving or fearful apprehension. It was so natural at the time that I scarcely noticed it, taking it as a matter of course. Later I realised that, without this mercy, he could have been tormented by the fear of that pain returning, and through him we would have been tormented too. Now he was carefree and fairly confident.

The time came to visit the consultant in Canterbury, who hadn't seen William since he recovered. The contrast between the cheerful, fresh complexioned young man before him, and the semi-conscious pain racked figure he had examined that evening in December, must have been very marked. The specialist told me that all there was left to show for the illness was the slight nautical roll in his walk, which we both agreed was rather attractive. He obviously marvelled at his health and said, 'I would tentatively put forward the word 'miracle'. What do you think?' I agreed, and after some persuasion told him of William's reading from Thessalonians. But I was surprised. Until then I had associated miracles with the instantaneous.

I was of the water into wine school; this had all been so gradual, so natural. I had seen his bodily strength and his relationship with God grow side by side, and I had thanked God from the bottom of my heart. But it had been hard work for all of us, and we had been so involved, there had never been time to sit back and think 'We've had a miracle.' Rather we felt that through Jesus we had had a deep experience of the love and reality of God. I suppose in a way that is what miracles are.

After the examination William had been pronounced fit to drive, so it was he who drove me home rejoicing. I sat there thinking over the words of the consultant. Yes of course it was a miracle, a miracle for a time; he wouldn't be twenty for another six months.

Wye agreed to take him back as a day student and the old Hillman Imp was in business once more, ferrying to and fro between lectures. Old relationships were soon re-established and he was often out in the evenings. Or friends would call and they would go to the pub in the village, where darts and bar billiards were the great challenge. He wanted to start farming again and persuaded David to allow him to feed the calves each morning before he set off. We were not sure how much he could do, and tried to keep the other farm work to a minimum.

I think because of his diminished strength he sometimes found the days long, and then the overflowing energy and high spirits of some of the students could grate on his nerves. He told me he was still carrying the little olive-wood cross which had been his comfort in illness. When he felt irritated he slipped his hand into his pocket, apparently just the feel of it helped.

So for a few weeks we were at peace, able to slip back into a more normal way of life, able to make a quick dash to Devonshire for Jane's wedding. She was an obviously happy bride; since the diagnosis she hadn't had a day's illness or discomfort. Her young bridegroom knew the cause of her anaemia, but for Jane and the uninitiated of her guests it was a happy, carefree day, a beautiful wedding. I am glad we were there.

There was a good film on in Canterbury a day or two after we got back, so we went to the cinema. I can't remember what the film was, but I still remember the pain of the return to real life after one or two hours oblivion watching it. Like putting a numbed hand into hot water, my whole being ached as reality flooded back. The diversion wasn't worth the price exacted. It seemed there was no cheap way to opt out, even for a few hours.

Neither he nor we knew how much William could safely do, though we all suspected over exertion might lead to trouble (and he became sure of that over the next few months, as his Journal shows). When trouble first came, it came like a thunderbolt, so sudden, unwelcome and unexpected. David and I arrived home in the car one day to see William leaning out of an upstairs window, unable to straighten to get in. A most distressing sight. He had come home from Wye in pain and not finding us upstairs, opened a window to call, hoping we were outside, but we weren't. He must have been there ten minutes or more. We got him in, and to bed, where high fever and pain reduced him to semi-consciousness in a few hours. Over the next few months there were to be several of these horrifying sharp attacks, each lasting for a few days and each leaving him a little weaker than the last. If he was out, the build up gave him enough time to get home, so that, in between, his life could continue much as before. It was a phase which may have been more taxing for us than for him. I didn't feel able to leave the house for long when David was at work. I couldn't risk William coming back unexpectedly to find no source of help — as he had that first time. Each attack was different from the last, and each to us seemed more gruelling. Mercifully, as after the first healing, William had no memory of the appalling pain, but I had, and each time I was shaken to the depths of my being.

A practical technique evolved to help us cope with these crises for him and for ourselves. It was really the age old combination of skilled medical help and prayer. The medical help came from the same marvellous team of doctors, the prayer was twofold. During the worst of his last illness it had become natural to hold him in our arms and pray together against the pain and sickness; now if the tide seemed to have turned against him as it often did, we would get in touch by phone with people, part of whose life's work it is to pray for the sick. I know his extra-ordinary recoveries surprised the doctors many times. It seemed that the 'specialist' prayer of people experienced in intercession, and not emotionally involved in William's illness, had great efficacy at times of crisis.

On one such occasion, unconsciousness, a temperature of 105° and stertorous breathing had persisted for many hours. After his examination the doctor told me that William had suffered a partial stroke, and that I could expect his mind to have been affected. He was sure I would need help with the nursing and that William would be in no condition to notice the change over. He called next morning to find his patient sitting up, reading the Times, with his breakfast, and asking to be allowed up that afternoon. Leukaemia is notoriously unpredictable most people agree, but not, I think, as unpredictable as that.

At this point, between attacks there might be weeks of normal living. One week-end we had some old friends from America to stay. William seemed relaxed and well. We were chatting about it as I drove them to the station. On my return I found Helena incoherent with tears, trying to ring the doctor from the phone in the hall. She had been sitting with William in the drawing room when he suddenly had an epileptic fit. At her age it was a dreadful experience which was to haunt her for months. Kneeling beside William a few minutes later, I felt deeply grieved at all she and he were going through. I had tried to protect her so hard. My mind turned back to the specialist who had made the initial undiscussed decision to arrest the illness when it would have been fatal in a few days. I wondered if he would change his mind if he had heard all that had happened since.

William recovered quite quickly, and never had another fit, but of course he couldn't drive until the specialist was convinced there would be no recurrence. I became chauffeur for the Wye College run.

While he was well and at Wye there was time to pray and take stock of our position for what lay ahead. We both realised that we badly needed a ground floor bedroom, one which would be easily accessible, without the cost to William's strength of climbing the stairs; one out of earshot of the rest of the family. We knew David's study made a good sickroom, as we had nursed an old lady there years before, but how to prepare a sick room and get a suitable bed moved in, while William was up and about, carefree about his short illnesses, and apparently well? Once he was ill it would be too late, there would be no moving him then.

That problem was solved in the most unexpected way, one which proved a blessing, though at the time it was a shock. David had an accident at work which ruptured the front tendon on his leg, detaching it from the knee cap. It meant an operation and three weeks in bed with the leg in plaster, so there was reason for a downstairs bedroom at once, and after a few days he was happily installed in it. Farming with teaching is a demanding combination which took most of his physical and mental energy. It must have been one of the first times for years that he was able to read, think and relax at leisure. He really needed that time to come to terms with all that had happened to us.

During those three peaceful weeks the Lord answered the need of his heart, which was to accept Jesus and commit his life to him. So literally with one blow we had a downstairs bedroom, David committed to Christ, and his wounded leg improved by the operation! It seemed that all our practical needs were to be met. Other things had scarcely formulated themselves in my mind before they were wonderfully supplied. It happened so naturally that it wasn't until afterwards I realised how we had been provided for. We were going to need help in the house when William was ill, but it had to be given by someone who could come in without being fetched, who would sympathise with the situation, and tolerate our unpredictable life style; so that whatever happened the basic minimum of cooking and cleaning would get done. It needed to be a loving person with a comforting presence. We knew that in term time, with the others away, if William was ill Helena would need all the support and company she could get. Mrs. Langford, an old friend who had come in over the years the children were small, suddenly wrote from London, saying that she wanted to move back to the village. A small cottage close by had just become vacant, and in a few weeks she had settled there, able to come in any morning we needed her. A blessing to the whole family.

Then Antoine, a young Swiss horticultural student, came to live with us for a year. I was in two minds when his mother, a distant cousin of David's suggested it, and I wrote explaining the situation. But if God had sorted through all the horticultural students in Europe, he couldn't have found a better one for us. A couple of years older than William, one of a big family, he slipped into ours like a hand into a glove. Both company for William, when he was well, and an affectionate, reassuring presence for Helena when he was ill.

Another small blessing was 'Turdus', Jamie's tame blackbird. He found him at the pink skin and down stage, the sole survivor in a nest of abandoned fledglings, and brought him home, just covered in short brown feathers, with the stumpy beginnings of a tail. I didn't imagine he would survive long in a house with two cats, but then I wouldn't have imagined he could have been reared successfully in an old biscuit tin kept under the bedclothes at night; but he survived and grew on a diet of bread and milk with chopped worms. His vociferous demands for food started at dawn and kept on almost unabated till dusk. Once he was able to make short flights about the kitchen he developed novel appetites, and we soon learnt the foods he liked best from his determined efforts to get them. He had strong tastes and a constitution of iron. Cheese, sardines, roast meat, kippers and plum jam were among his favourites. He had a keen sense of smell, and if I opened the oven door when chicken or meat were roasting, he would be there in a flash, as close to the roasting pan as he dared. Jamie used to try and educate him in all that blackbirds really eat, showing him worms in the ground, and as many other edible insects as they could uncover together, encouraging the first short planing flights he took from the palm of his hand.

At the time of William's journal, Turdus was adolescent. He flew short distances and was starting to explore outside the window for himself, often overestimating his flying power and getting lost or stuck. To begin with, uncertain of his identity, he joined a flock of early morning starlings on their roost. He found himself flying off with them and barely made it home that evening, he was so exhausted. After that I checked their tree each morning, peering up into the branches like an over-anxious mother trying to protect her child from the undesirable children next door! I didn't let him out until they had gone.

Turdus was still dark brown with a brown beak, but immature as he was, he fell precociously in love with a hen blackbird; thus resolving his identity crisis and our uncertainty as to his sex. That first unsuccessful courtship was conducted from the safety of our kitchen; several times he came plummeting home through the window with an irate rival cock bird on his tail. There was even one windowsill confrontation with an angry male rapping at the pane at him through the glass. His conversational vocabulary made up of little unmusical staccato notes, was very companionable to hear when we were both digging in the garden, but better still was when he came and sang from the top of the dresser while I cooked the supper. First it was a lovely muffled sub song, sung from the throat without opening the beak. Then as he grew older the glorious liquid notes of the adult bird. We grew to know each phrase and heard his song evolve as he changed and added to them. When he was outside we could tell his song from among all the others. He would come down from his tree in answer to our whistle.

We first realised he had mated and was feeding young when he landed on the table one meal time carrying a caterpillar and a crane fly in his beak. Putting them down he skewered a scrap of meat, picked them up again and was off. We found his family in the clematis near the kitchen window. After that he was constantly in and out for scraps; sometimes I trembled for his young when I saw what he took them, bits of crust, lumps of cheese rind, scraps of gristle. He seemed prepared to push anything down their gaping throats. His wife must have thought she had married a millionnaire, the supply was so plentiful.

Turdus lived in and out of our house for eight years. He knew us all individually and our bedroom windows; if David and I overslept he would be in on our bed to call us.

We finally knew he had died when his distracted widow mother of fledglings started coming indoors looking for food. We all missed him and will always be grateful to Jamie for the experience of knowing a wild bird so intimately. I think perhaps he was more than a small blessing.

7: How much longer

College term was ending. William had been an intermittent student, but we knew he would badly miss the focus Wye had given his life, the occupation and companionship he found there. Now his strength was limited and any over exertion could precipitate an illness, there was less and less he was able to do at home. He had always been an active person; if he was up he expected to be busy at something. The great battle against boredom he was to fight to the day of his death was about to begin, and I for one was very apprehensive. We racked our brains for occupations and enquired among friends, with no success. It was an anxiety meriting star rating in our prayers. We dreaded him getting bored and then depressed; so we were relieved and deeply grateful when he came up with some engrossing new occupations for himself, things we wouldn't have dreamed of. Wine and jam making were the first; they turned out to be perfect interests for that time, useful, creative and time consuming. I think he did the cooking in the light of his experience in the school chemistry lab. Once picked, each ingredient was meticulously weighed, measured and recorded; the recipe followed in minutest detail. Some triumphantly good jam resulted; we were still using it the year after he died. The wine was less reliable, some good, some frankly disgusting, but all worth its weight in gold as a pastime for the maker. After he had died the bottles, with his hand written message on each lable, were to be a heart-stopping part of my store cupboard.

William was in bed recovering from one of his horrible short illnesses when he had the idea of keeping a journal,

55

and David bought the first of the five hard backed note books which he was to fill, with the thoughts and feelings of those last four months of his life. That journal was to be a great solace to him, always to hand when he had time to occupy, a ready outlet for the feelings he spared us. He had never shown the slightest pleasure in writing before, so we thanked God for this new interest. There was hardly a day on which he didn't record something, even at his worst a few drunken words would be scrawled across the page. It is easier to tell from the writing than his words how ill he was at times. He wrote in the journal until the day before he died; on that last day he could only dictate.

Thomas Merton's 'Sign of Jonas', written from the confines of a Trappist monastery, was a book that delighted William and inspired him to attempt his journal. He had been very moved by the life and writings of Richard Wurmbrand also; two very different men, one a Roman Catholic monk, the other a Roumanian Baptist pastor. Wurmbrand's sermons memorised in the solitary confinement of an underground cell, where he suffered years of physical deprivation, torture and beatings, were full of his love for God. I thought later that in his humble way William had something in common with both authors; he too recorded a confined, restricted life, later to be imprisoned by illness, with all the physical deprivation and suffering that brought; he too was sustained by the love of God.

Life took an upward swing with the start of the school holidays. Jamie, Helena and David were at home; Angela back from teaching practice and Liz too, to be with us, doing a physiotherapy job in the local hospital. So William had plenty of company and was appreciating it all, as his journal shows. But understandably the doctors were not so happy. I suppose he was a bit of a medical enigma at that time, having no reason to be alive. Suddenly they confronted us with the need to make a devastating decision. We were asked to consent to his being admitted to a new

56

cancer research unit in a London teaching hospital. There he would be barrier-nursed, and his illness completely reinvestigated. My blood ran cold as I imagined what this would mean to him, leaving home to return to dreaded hospital where he would be isolated from all direct human contact while he was subjected to more painful tests. To be told that this was the last ditch treatment for cancer, an experimental attempt to prolong his restricted life. Perhaps he would even die there, cut off from home, and everything he loved. We asked for time to think. I was frightened, frightened that this plan could be put into operation whatever we felt. I could see that it made medical sense, and that was more frightening still.

I tried to consider it objectively. We thought, prayed, and discussed it with a doctor friend, but my mind and heart were adamant. When our time was up, we met with the doctors round our dining room table. I found myself having to tell them that William had only six weeks left before his final illness. I said God had told me in a dream; I didn't feel up to going into details about memorial stones! They were both extremely gentle and sensitive as always to our feelings; no doubt they thought that anxiety had unbalanced my mind a little, but they never showed it. Later the head of a cancer research project was consulted; to our relief he said that if it were his son, he would think as we did; so the danger was over; William had those last weeks at home.

I wonder if either of the doctors had remembered what I said about his final illness when, six weeks later, the hospital put through an urgent call, because William's blood count had dropped so dramatically. It was October 8th, the day after his twentieth birthday. We celebrated that birthday on a Saturday, two days late, because we all wanted to be there. It was lucky we were given that; it was the last for which he was well enough to be out of bed. The following morning the drop in his blood count was beginning to take effect. He was incapacitated by pain in one leg. By the fourteenth, five days later, he was desperately ill. It was one of several days, to come at different times during this illness, that I spent sitting by his bed, an open mind whether he was going to live or not. The Lord was very good to me at those times, helping me feel so sure of him that I could be at peace while I watched and waited. This silent, peaceful presence was a necessity for William. It was no good letting my mind wander or distracting myself with a book. To hold this peace I had to stay as close to Jesus as I could. I have discovered since that this is a gift we can share with all the dying.

Leaving William once after such a crisis, to dash to the village for a last minute necessity, I wondered at feeling so light hearted. Open minded and accepting I might have been, but now my whole being rejoiced that he was still at home for me to go back to.

It was a strange way of life, and not easy to deal with conversationally, on the rare occasions I was out. Few enquirers had any idea of the depths concealed by 'Oh much better thank you'. How could they?

William's thoughts and feelings went into his journal. The irritation, depression and frustration he managed to spare us are all recorded there. He was never cut off from the life of the house except when he wanted to be. Cats, dogs, friends, relations, even Turdus, occasionally felt free to drop in and out of his downstairs bedroom. Many times we thought he was about to die, yet when it came we were not expecting it.

He was unconcerned by the prospect of death. I knew this from a conversation I had with him at the time of an appalling throat infection (Oct. 19th). Discussing it next morning we agreed together that at times we had both wondered if he would survive the night. I said, 'You do realise that you might die at any time, don't you?' And he answered 'Yes, of course, I've known that for years.' Reassured I said no more, but perhaps at that time I should have told him exactly what was wrong: he could have stopped fighting the disease, and spared himself some of the weeks that lay ahead. The two daytime dreams he recorded on October 18th have confirmed this in my mind; re-reading them I realise that they represent his two major illnesses. In the first the prisoner is forgiven, blessed, healed and released, but in the second Jesus is telling him to throw away his weapons, stop fighting the illness, and make the leap to where His love was waiting. He never realised it, but those prayers in his journal were mostly abundantly answered. For the last weeks of his life he radiated peace, gaiety and love; love which we felt in his concerned unselfishness for us and anyone with whom he was in contact. I am sure it was this that ministered to us as we cared for him.

By the end his body, though not his face, was terribly emaciated. His back was covered with bruises and the rest of him with a rash of dull purple spots where capillary blood vessels were collapsing. For six weeks he bled unceasingly from the nose, and down the throat. It was soon impossible to give him morphine by injection because he could bleed for hours from even so tiny a wound. His weakness gradually made him almost completely dependent on us for movement. Yet to do anything for him, to give him a bed bath for instance, was always a happy experience. He seemed to draw on an inexhaustable well of gaiety, an inner source of real happiness, quite apart from courage, which bubbled up at most unlikely times, in the face of insuperable odds. That was what kept my heart from breaking as I watched the deterioration, and gradual disintegration of his body. Instead, as each new symptom appeared, I could feel gladness that it marked another step nearer his final release, and to Jesus whom he loved.

Early in November David was given time off to be with William for what remained of his life. He badly needed his company, and I needed his help, though I had managed well until then. It was wonderful what resources of strength, energy and confidence I had been given, and I believed the supply would be there for both of us as long as we were in need. Without that, the broken nights, the piles of extra washing, with the day to day running of our house and the constant care for William would have been too much. One weekend I remember particularly. Upstairs David, immobilized in bed with a strained back, was suffering the dire effects of mild arsenical poisoning from a sheep dip, while downstairs William fought his way through another grave crisis. As he left that evening, the doctor remarked that I looked a little tired! I felt I had every right; even the soles of my feet felt worn out. It was surely a blessing that I didn't look worse!

Even if William hadn't disliked the idea of a nurse, and if we hadn't wanted to look after him ourselves, we still would have been unlikely to get help. There were no Marie Curie nurses within reach at that time and we couldn't afford agency fees. With a sleeping bag on a camp bed by William's door, I found I could get several hours sleep a night; David looked after him in the afternoons, so then I could make up what I had missed.

We hadn't enquired too closely what form the last stages of the illness were likely to take. We didn't want to agonise over all the possibilities. Somewhere I heard that internal bleeding might destroy his sight or affect his brain, and from that moment I prayed very much that his eyes and brain would be spared. Although his sight worried him at times, he was able to see and think clearly to the end.

It wasn't until the last three days that I started to wonder how much longer we could all go on. William was too stiff and weak to use his hands for more than a few minutes, and needed help with nearly every movement. Except for the tiny amount he joined in when David was doing handicrafts, the journal was the only form of activity he had left. He could only write a few lines of that at a time. His poor emaciated body was deteriorating visibly each day; soon there would be nothing he could do for himself. As I was thinking what that would mean to him, the last line of the Te Deum came into my mind: 'Oh God in you have I trusted: Let me never be confounded.' It expressed exactly what I was feeling and was the prayer of my heart. We had trusted and were still trusting, but each of us was growing tired. I didn't know that our journey was nearly over.

The end when it came was unexpected. He had had a restless night, but in the morning was as interested as ever in the previous day's plasticraft, and wanted me to show it to him as soon as he woke. David went off to feed the animals as usual; none of us realised that this was our last day together. William, who was lying rather flat, suddenly developed a breathing difficulty and needed to be lifted upright very quickly. There was no time to send for help. All I could do was to pray for strength. Then I lifted him smoothly and gently, and somehow set my back against his to support him till help arrived.

The last morning passed gently by, as many more had before it. There was no question of his writing that day as he was finally too weak, but he dictated a letter to accompany a paperweight he had made for John and Sally. The doctor took a grave view of William's breathing difficulties, but all of us had seen him far iller many times before. When the afternoon came I forced myself to go upstairs to sleep as usual, against another bad night to come.

After half an hour I felt too uneasy to stay there any longer. When I returned, William said, 'Ma, would you mind both sitting with me this afternoon, if you have nothing better to do?' I caught David's eye at that typical phrase. As if there could be anything better to do. I crept out once as he slept, to greet Liz and Helena who arrived home together. A minute later I returned. William was awake and fighting for breath. As I took his hand, which was icy cold, he murmured, 'I think I am going.' We just had time to kiss him goodbye before he lost consciousness. Twenty minutes later his body gave up its valiant fight for breath and he died. . .

For a little time David and I sat alone together in the adjoining room. Apart from shock we felt only peace and gratitude; no sense of loss, that would come later. Then we went to break the news to the family.

The few days before the funeral were too full of arrangements to allow much time to think. Even so I was surprised how sad I felt. I had longed for William's release, forgetting how desperately I would miss him when it came.

We wanted it to be a service of thanksgiving for his life, triumphant illness and death, and for the blessings poured upon us. It was difficult choosing the form the service should take during those first numb days, but some lines from John 14 caught my eye when we were looking for inspiration in William's New English Bible: 'Peace is my parting gift to you, my own peace, such as the world can not give. Set your troubled hearts at rest and banish your fears. You heard me say I am going away and coming back to you. If you loved me you would have been glad I was going to the Father. For the Father is greater than I. I have told you now beforehand so when it happens you may have faith.'

God had indeed told us beforehand, and what a wonder, joy and strength was the faith he gave to carry us through.

8: The underground stream

The funeral was over. It was time to pick up the broken fragments of our lives, and start again.

A small house on the wintry coast of Cornwall had been lent to us by friends and we went there that evening, wanting to be alone with our younger children before they faced their schools again. We had told Angela some weeks before that William could not recover, but the younger ones had continued to hope, and so were the more shocked.

If we had known anything about bereavement in those days we would have openly shared our grief then, but in our ignorance we hoped that our peace and acceptance would be enough to comfort and reassure them. Perhaps it did, but more than comfort they needed to express their own deep hurt and sense of loss. After that would have been the time for comfort. Unwittingly we helped to bury their grief, and so gave them a burden of unexpressed mourning to carry for many years.

Parents in our position do not always get bereavement counselling, and even now many may not know that the death of one child can leave another emotionally crippled by the guilt, anger and bitterness that are a normal part of unexpressed mourning. Sorrow needs to be shared at a deep level, and tears shed. They are part of the painful healing process which eventually leads to a full recovery. I can only thank the Lord that ours did not suffer more than they did.

If I had trusted Jesus for them as totally as I did for William, they would have been told the truth at the same time as Angela. Following my own judgement I mistakenly tried to protect them. The areas of failure were all my failures in trust.

While we were away it almost felt that William was still at home. Subconsciously I must have been able to fool myself some, though not all, of the time. Although it was December it was a great liberation to be out of doors again on that beautiful coast, to see the great Atlantic rollers crashing on to the beaches, and seals swimming through rough water near the shore. But seagulls wheeling in the grey skies above the estuary at St. Maws brought a moment of unutterable sadness; suddenly they were the gulls in the icy sky above William's Aberdeen hospital window, the ones we fed together when he was first ill. I could not wish him back for a minute, but I needed his company so much I wanted to die and end our separation. We had been close companions, dependent on each other in the fight against his illness. Now I was separated from him and left behind. I found it desperately hard.

The house was very empty when we got home. David, Jamie and Helena went back to school, and there was just the clearing up to be done. The downstairs bedroom to be turned back into a study, the familiar clothes to be disposed of and his bedroom redecorated. David dealt with the clothes.

I needed Christ's sustaining help as much then as I ever had. He was wonderfully good to me and I knew William was with him. It was just a question of adjusting to his absence. How well I understood Simeon's words to Mary, when she presented her baby son at the Temple. He prophesied that a sword was to pierce her heart also. In those first weeks, with Christ's help, I lived normally without too much sadness, until memory, like a sword thrust, would pierce my heart with a physical pain so intense I could scarcely breath or move. Simeon could have been given no better words to describe it.

There was a deep wound but it was clean and healthy. I had been saved the bitterness which could have slowed its healing, and my whole life had been enriched. Christ had become very real to me. I was learning to love and trust him in a way that I wouldn't have dreamt possible.

Burrswood was founded with a charge to 'heal the sick, give faith to the faithless and comfort the sorrowing' — in fact to be a practical expression of Christ's love in the world. There could be few more therapeutic places to work, returning part-time for three years was a privilege and education. Coming and going as I did, made it easier to notice the change in visitors and patients. There were a few instantaneous healings while I was there, but more often I saw Christ's love at work blessing and reconstructing shattered lives. It was a gradual process of liberation and healing within, which transformed attitudes and personalities and was most noticeable to the outsider. Contact with his love, through the Healing Services, and the loving care of the medical and nursing staff, speeded the recovery of many of the patients in the Nursing Home. Others were blessed with the faith and courage to face terminal illness. There were failures and difficulties, as there are in all human institutions. Not everyone was helped or healed, but I think only a tiny percentage did not feel they had been greatly blessed.

There were others, paraplegics, sufferers from muscular dystrophy, multiple schlerosis and other distressing progressive diseases, who returned each year to renew their spiritual strength. Strength to bear the frustrations, humiliations and dependencies of their illness. In spite, or perhaps because of this the atmosphere was cheerful, peaceful and above all optimistic.

The Rank Foundation had given a bursary for the care of children with leukaemia. Several families came while I was there, staying for a short time, so that each member could receive as much help as possible. Naturally I had a specially tender concern for them. Through my contact there, through a neighbouring doctor and friends, I got to know parents facing the problem we had faced. Shared experience gave us an immediate affinity which was invaluable. But because everyone is unique I had to learn to put this on one side, to really feel what was happening to them. The apostle Paul put it into words for me: 'Praise be to the God and Father of our Lord Jesus Christ, the Father of compassion and God of all comfort, who comforts us in all our troubles, so that we can comfort those in any trouble with the comfort we ourselves have received from God.' (2 Cor 1. 3,4). I was learning to do just that, it was joy and part of my own process of healing. That and being involved in so many other lives.

Jane, for whom we had been so anxious, was able to live a full and happy married life until the spring when she died at home after a short illness. She suffered no pain and was only in bed for a few days. We gave thanks for her gentle death, and for the courage of her parents.

Spending two days a week at Burrswood meant that the rest of my time was full. I was busy, involved, fully occupied, yet towards the end of that first year I started to sense a lack in my life. It wasn't William I was missing, I was familiar with that ache, it was Christ. I had started to miss the closer relationship I had had when I needed to turn to him for help and strength many times a day. The first lines of Psalm 63 expressed my feelings, and often came to my mind.

Oh God you are my God
Early will I seek you.
My soul thirsts for you.
My body longs for you.
As a dry and thirsty land, where no water is.
So longing I come before you in the sanctuary.
For your loving kindness is better than life itself.

It was partly to pray for the patients, and partly in search of this relationship, that I started spending the best part of my lunch hours at Burrswood in the Oratory. It was there that Christ answered my need. His Spirit came strongly upon me, as I prayed, and the language of my prayer suddenly changed. I was praying in tongues though I didn't know it. It took some careful enquiries and the help of a woman friend, for me to realise this new blessing. A few years before I believed that miracles and healing were a thing of the past. If I had considered it at all, I would have thought the same about the gift of tongues. But if believers needed and received it in the Acts of the Apostles, why shouldn't they now? God doesn't change. The conventional, middle-aged side of my nature was rather shocked, but my true being rejoiced, and does till this day. It has been a wholesome, peaceful, joyful gift; an underground stream always there, always running, to refresh, renew and bless. Living water, not for my sake alone, but for others. I had been very thirsty and exactly as he promised, Christ refreshed me.

It is eleven years since Jane and William died; so much has happened since. There have been times of difficulty and sorrow, as well as much happiness and joy. But now we can accept whatever comes with hope, knowing that Jesus is always able to bring good out of evil, to bless the worst circumstances, if we will to trust him, hold fast to him and keep the way open.

The children are grown up now. Two have married and have children of their own. We shall always lack the love and affection William would have given us, and I shall never cease to miss him. But when I look back on my life before he was ill, I see it as a poor shadow of what has come through his illness. The new life Christ has poured into mine, is so real, so abundant. Through him I find new people to love everywhere. In all walks of life, all denominations, I recognise and am recognised by my brothers and sisters. The old divisions and barriers have melted. I feel his love within me stretch out to those who suffer. He gives me strength to nurse the dying and comfort the bereaved. I know that he can use me to bring hope, to reassure and strengthen, sometimes to heal.

Alone in Aberdeen during those first days of William's illness, I prayed desperately to a far away God I didn't know, who perhaps heard my prayers, but didn't answer. An awesome God enthroned in power and might, whom I should meet on the day of judgement. How could I get in touch with him? But in Christ he got in touch with me. He found me in my grief and fear, shared my burdens and blessed my life. Now I can feel his love and know the joy of being his child, able to approach him in confidence and trust, knowing that when I pray in his will, my prayers are answered.

I have hesitated to write these last paragraphs for fear I should seem an exceptionally spiritual person, when the joy is that I am not. Watchman Nee, in what William called his 'Women's Institute stale cake' title, describes my experience as The Normal Christian Life. Christ lives in me, I am a branch of the Vine, still self-centred, scatter-brained, shy, proud, greedy, acquisitive and a hundred other things, but he is working on that! Meanwhile I have the joy of his kingdom within me.

This is the great blessing that came out of those agonising years for us. The blessing held out to all who suffer, and don't we all? Christ is very close to us then, whatever our beliefs. He didn't opt out of the suffering in this world, and still shares it with us. The power of his cross can bless all our hardship and pain, even the suffering we bring on ourselves through sin. When he says, 'Take up your cross and follow me', this is the gift and the blessing he offers. Without him, suffering can destroy, but with him it brings life, his life more abundantly.

William's Journal

Saturday, July 24th, 1971

At last I have my note book I have wanted it for two whole days. A book in which I can write about thoughts and deeds and then in three days time when I have run out of ideas, I can read it through and think what awful artificial twaddle — I hope that doesn't happen.

The whole idea of this book came from Thomas Merton's *The Sign of Jonas*. A truly brilliant book. Almost makes me want to become a Monk. I have actually thought of going into the Church, but don't think it is quite right for me, or I am not quite right for it yet. I have a long way to go. When I think about myself and Christianity and the amount I know and put into practice I feel very very small indeed. Yesterday I saw an ant crawling over the rush matting in Pa's study, which is my bedroom while I am ill. It was a great effort for the tiny chap. That's how I feel. I pray that I could be more at one with God, with him the whole day, to be able to have the ability to see him and love him in everything. This should be my whole lifetime's aim. I presume that is what life is all about, seeing him in everything and doing his will.

M. ten minutes ago asked what I wanted for lunch — as I have an upset stomach, 'Anything,' said I thoughtlessly. She has just gone back to the kitchen to boil me an egg. I know that I don't appreciate Ma and Pa enough. They have nursed me on and off since October '70. I always think this in bed. Wait until I get up and they tell me I can't do this and I can't do that because I am convalescing. I always know this is going to happen and I prepare myself for it, I must try harder.

Since I have been reading Merton I have had a

marvellous inner peace which I have never had before, I wonder what it is?

Being in bed is marvellous for contemplation, you get such a lot of time to yourself. Wait till I get up, all will change then — I will rush at everything trying to take all life, and my prayers, at a gallop; I must learn to be temperate in the fullest meaning of the word as described in *Divine Pity*. Everything I have is from God, therefore I should do everything for God, but do I? I do it for myself.

It is a wild day outside with a very grey sky. I don't need to look out of the window to know what it looks like. All the corn is turning, and as the sky is so grey, the grass and trees look marvellously dark green. At least the rain has come; the first proper rain for about three weeks. That lovely smell of damp earth and wet trees is coming in the window — how glorious.

Sunday, July 25th

Dull grey windy day. I woke up this morning at 9.30. I always feel cheated of the day when I wake up so late.

This morning's first Old Testament reading was great fun. With the second I found that I had read it accidentally yesterday, but I read yesterday's and today's, and something that made no sense yesterday made sense to-day — strange.

Helena just told me that she has something for me. She emptied her pocket, out came a handful of hay and straw mixture, a piece of string, and finally my gift, some shells from Seasalter. On my bed afterwards I found a rabbit's dropping.

> Pray as you can and do not try to pray as you can't.
> Take yourself as you find yourself; start from that.
> > *Dom Chapman*

I have just decided that I don't really want to get up. The reason is not that I am lazy but that when I do get up I will not be able to do enough, and I will be open to those

70

awful curses of frustration and consequently bad tempered. Life becomes unpleasant for everybody, especially Ma – I must try harder.

The sky isn't so overcast now, but the wind seems to be getting more and more fresh. The swifts and doves love it, they are all wheeling about with the greatest abandon.

The view outside the window this evening was absolutely breath-taking; the sun was coming from the northwest and all the shadows were long. The sky was dark blue. The corn was orange yellow and the trees were every shade of green from dark oak to light willow. My words and adjectives are useless to describe the beauty. The rain has come bringing with it a dark grey mist, and a bright rainbow which lands in Elvey Field. I hope that I will be able to freeze the beauty of that sight in my mind for ever. God is good to the countryside. The rain comes so hard now that the view is obliterated.

As I prayed, I prayed that Jesus might lead me. I had a vivid picture of a grassy track through a birchwood, you could see the bark on the trees, the grass was wet on the feet. I was being led up a slight slope, being led by the hand, and also there was an arm around my shoulder. I felt wonderfully comforted, warm and loved. Just being led up that slope I never got to the summit. The wet path up must have been life. The top? Not death, just the future. It was one of those slopes which you always think that you are reaching the top of, but when you get there, there is one more summit to go, you hope – so it goes on. I will regret putting this in I know.

Monday, July 26th
Peace at last. The vacuum cleaner has left my room. I am sure that machine defeats its own object by sucking the dust so hard that it is sucked right through and blown out the back. Like a great deal of modern machinery it does things quicker but not so well. It makes a great deal of noise, anyway I think that is what M. likes. I am sure it

gives her a great feeling of having done something very industrious. The spiders suffer, they don't stand a chance, but they keep breeding valiantly on.

The cat has just come in the window. Always a welcome visitor, but rather a wet one this time, so he has sat himself on the floor, and is licking himself dry — difficult task.

Merton quotes Thoreau in his *Walden*:

I went to the woods because I wished to live deliberately,
to front only the essential facts of life, and see if I could not learn what it had to teach and not, when I come to die, discover that I had not lived.

I went outside at noon and I sat down. Everything was wildly beautiful. I wanted to be able to write about it, the skirl of the wind and the broken clouds filtering the sun, but I think a lack of words is more eloquent than anything that I could say. By writing many things down that are personally beautiful, I destroy that beauty, but I never know what is going to be destroyed until it is written.

I got up for lunch, my knees still hurt. I must turn the pain and confinement to useful things. I must teach myself not to champ at the bit for activity because that only brings frustration and general discomfort for everybody. Also activity brings temptation. The spirit is willing but the flesh (if it could be called such) is abominably weak.

Confusion and fog pile up in your life and then by the power of the Cross things once again are clear and you know more about your wretchedness and you are grateful for another miracle.

Thomas Merton

I know nothing, I am as ignorant as mud, maybe it is not ignorance but the inability to understand. Where is the borderline between ignorance and the inability to understand? If only I could understand, I feel as though I am missing something vital. There is an emptiness in my life. If only I could fill it; I can't do it on my own, God must help.

Very sad to say I have finished *The Sign of Jonas,* I feel as if a part of me was gone. I have suddenly realised that I am busily trying to find questions to answer. How foolish, but if you didn't ask questions, where would you be? It is a paradox you have to think of questions to ask yourself, if you don't you get nowhere, but you can't answer the main question yourself, you can answer hardly any of them. What is this emptiness in my life? What am I missing that should be so much a part of me? Lord Your only answer is emptiness. I will wait.

Outside the window Jamie is busily talking to his blackbird, showing him ants, etc. and telling him heatedly to eat them up. Great characters, J. and his bird.

Christ died for me. I died with him. The sinner, like Adam in me died with Christ in the tomb. As I died with him I was also resurrected with him as part of the new second man. The old was dead, the new was alive. The new was Christ, and I was with him. Therefore I am as nothing, Christ lives in me. My body is just a shell, a house for the Christ that is in me. 'Abide in Christ.'

I have not got to make myself a branch, the Lord Jesus tells me I am a branch. I am part of him and I have just to believe it and act upon it. I have seen it long enough in the Bible, but I believe it now as a living reality.

Tuesday, July 27th

A very ordinary morning, overcast and slightly misty. The fact that I think it is ordinary confirms the feelings of dissatisfaction I can feel building up in me. The feeling that I want to get up and go out, but any effort that way will be completely frustrated. This causes the feeling I have, I must just contain it for a fortnight and I might be able to start having a slightly more normal existence. Writing this helps a lot, it takes out the bottled up energy and compression inside. I feel as if I may be doing something vaguely useful. It is a good safety valve anyway, I feel better already. Who would have ever thought of me writing for pleasure? It was a possibility I have never even considered in my life. I, who can't string more than a couple of phrases together; I, who can't punctuate or express myself in words to save my life. I feel though that this what-ever-it-is, has a purpose. I wonder what it is? When I say a purpose I mean more than just a time consumer. It is being done for some particular reason which is beyond me. I am enjoying myself greatly and as far as I am concerned that is what counts. A selfish attitude I know, but that is just how I feel at present. I feel happy, thank God. I now feel, why should I drag God into it, but there he is with all his love and concern for everyone of us. That is why he is there, three lines up, He desperately cares for us but we don't know it or can't feel it.

Sitting out here under the ash tree is proving quite a trial. The flies and thunderbugs form a pestilential veil around me. Nice to know one is wanted and appreciated by someone, however small they may be. The whole of my shirt is covered with thunderbugs. What concerns me is what in their wiggly way are they after? Can I offer them something so particular that they have to infest me in this way? They look so lethal crawling around waving their bottoms like they do, I don't think that they bite. If they are after my blood, I am afraid that I will have to turn on the offensive and stop their gymnastic existence. They have now started exploring down the inside of my shirt, a little tickly but they are welcome to explore, if they dare. They obviously can't know what is in store for them. That's enough I think about thunderbugs. I have really got quite attached to them in the last few minutes. May they go on enjoying my infestation.

Roped into shelling peas. Food for thought, fingers and stomach. Quite a healthy occupation. The Devil makes

74

work for idle hands, maybe I ought to work in a pea factory.

I lie here on my bed in beautiful peace, the only things to disturb it are the birds, the flies and my clock. The birds are all seething with life and noise in their heedless quest for food, while the flies seem content to buzz around and around, occasionally trying to destroy themselves against the window panes. A fruitless and dull life but they all seem to have accepted it. My clock ticks on. What do dogs, cows or sheep think about as they lie around? Why is it that I need this constant activity?

It really is pouring and the whole scene looks thoroughly autumnal except for the corn, that looks dark brown and very wet. I have a dog sitting beside me — a very wet dog making polite enquiries whether it can come up on my bed, poor thing.

Jamie's bird has just had a narrow escape — he got out and was lost in this pouring rain. He was eventually found by M., looking very small, wet and bedraggled. She dried him with a hair dryer.

Wednesday, July 28th

Last night the cat came in much earlier than usual at about twelve o'clock, and lay silently on my bed, and didn't bother me one bit until about half past six, when we both woke up. He is a lovely friend and company.

This morning Angela, M. and I are going to Communion I hope. This is one of the few times that I have ever really wanted to go or felt that I really need to go, but it having been revealed that Christ and the Holy Spirit are in me, I feel that communion is rather like baptism, a declaration that one is nothing but what Christ gives you. A declaration of one's servantship to Christ and a submission to his will. I am sure these are all the wrong reasons, but at present they are mine.

Just had another escape with J's blackbird. It flew on to the top of the woodshed. I sat below and kept guard while

J. slid all over the roof — it really was very good entertainment. J. got the bird on his hand, started coming down; the bird, who is of an independent nature, decided to fly back again, this happened two or three times. We got him in the end.

The Communion was lovely; the church peaceful and quiet. I think more of the idea of praise ought to enter into the Communion, but who am I to start questioning that which has satisfied man and God since King James' time, or whenever the Prayer Book was printed. I feel that one ought to ask forgiveness by thanking the Lord for having forgiven you. My own will must be thrown aside. I must realise that I am capable of nothing without him because he is me.

My feline friend has just walked in through the door and has proceeded to chase flies. I wonder what they taste like? I imagine them to be rather nutty and spicey in flavour. Most of the other people's corn looks mid brown. I find it very satisfying to look at, knowing that we don't have any. I shouldn't feel any satisfaction at all, I know, I should just feel sympathy but I can't for some reason. It is rather like when one hears about a disaster like a plane crash, I can't feel a great deal of sorrow — should we be able to? or do we have a safety device installed to stop us feeling personal loss for the suffering. I presume if one did feel a great deal at every disaster one would be in a pretty sorry state. Maybe it is a character one developes as one becomes more concerned for other people. Thinking of them as relatives in Christ (I don't like that expression 'brothers and sisters' — too brown and musty), then one would feel personal loss.

Watchman Nee's book *Normal Christian Life* has been to me a revelation. It is very unfortunate that it should have that title, which is enough to put many people off. The only reasons that I am reading it is that M. recommended it, explaining that the title was very misleading. The title now holds no horror at all, and I can only feel excitement at it, but I do remember having that feeling of 'Women's Institute stale cake' when I heard it.

Why is it that I always have so much more to say and do in the morning? Yesterday I did all the work in the morning and come the afternoon I was completely stumped for anything to say at all. I have come to the conclusion that I don't like the afternoons, they are merely hours to be filled in between lunch and tea; that isn't the way one should feel.

I have just had a feeling that I will never make the christian grade. The standards are too high and the way too long, but I also know for a fact that Christ has done, and will do, everything for me — so what is the problem? Faith I should think. If I just have faith there is no problem at all, that is what I have to remember. Remember that and I can do anything that is required of me by the will of God.

Had a marvellous afternoon for a change. Smoking and playing cards, very unlike Watchman Nee's friend who couldn't play cards because his hands weren't his — they were God's.

Looks like and feels like more rain. It is so close that one can almost get a handful of the atmosphere and throw it. Thunderbugs pretty active too. They like to play hide and seek on the black and whiteness of my page.

Thursday, July 29th

A pleasant morning, slightly chilly after yesterday's rain. The countryside looks much recovered, the trees look darker and the corn looks a deeper yellow, the whole view is covered by a fine steam.

The Old Testament readings are becoming much more enjoyable since the advent of Elisha, full of action and drama, and so well written. I wonder who was the Chronicler at that time, and what were his reasons for writing down the doings of Elisha. It always interests me that the Chroniclers should take a much healthier interest in the doings of the Prophets, than the gaddings about of the Kings. For instance all the mention that one king gets is that he reigned for twelve years and was the son of so and so. How did the chroniclers know that the doings of people like Elisha should be so much more important than the petty carryings on of the kings of that time. The substance of the Old Testament is gripping but I find it very difficult to get a message from. The only message seems to be the unlimited capabilities of someone who has faith.

I think I might have reintroduced M. to the possibility that I might be smoking again. She came asking for matches and I told her to take them from my tobacco tin, in it were matches, cigarette papers and tobacco. I wonder if she has come to the only conclusion possible? The trouble with Ma is that one can never know how much she knows. One always thinks one's parents are awfully foolish, but they never are as foolish as one would like them to be.

This morning I am in a terrible rush to get up and be doing things. I can feel it building up inside of me. This feeling is what is going to kill everything beneficial that might have happened to my spirit in the last few days. Let's hope it doesn't, it would be such a waste of time. Maybe this scribbling will tide me over, who knows, I have never tried this sort of thing before. There is a first time for everything, I must stop writing now because I must go upstairs and have a bath and wash my hair which has been smelling lately. I never had this problem before it all fell out. Maybe it has a new sort of juice on it, where it is growing through — what a disgusting thought. Well whatever it is it is going to be washed off this morning and for the next few days I must walk around looking like a guard outside Buckingham Palace. Aren't I self-conscious, one would have thought that losing one's hair would have killed any self esteem I ever had. But no, what is it and why is it that one is so conscious about one's appearance. Isn't what I was given good enough? One should never have to rely on one's outward appearance. I take it as a sign that one isn't quite sure that what is inside is any good or would stand up to a close scrutiny. In fact people who constantly worry about their physical appearance are unstable and can only rely, or think they can, on their outward appearance.

Leaving this page with something that everybody else has realised for years, I will make haste to my bath.

Everybody is going out leaving M. behind with me. That is pretty grim. Enough to make me fume, why can't they leave me alone, I am perfectly capable of looking after myself — who the hell do they think I am, some sort of manic depressive who is going to cut his throat! They are going the right way to turn me into one. The only place I can take out my anger is on these putrid pages — thank heavens I have them, otherwise I would be pretty foul company by now. The thing about these lines is that I can pour my spleen out on them rather than on everybody else. There, that's all my fury gone safely absorbed into these pages. I wonder how I will fare if I go back into the kitchen. Just the sight of M., or the thought of the sight of her, makes me feel cross, which is totally unfair. All I have to do is leave it to him. I know I can't do it but he can — that was proved to me last night by Watchman Nee. I must just resign myself to his care and all will be all right, which is a nice thought. I needn't worry or try at all. Angela has just come in like a breath of fresh air to wish me luck.

They have all gone, I have just spent ten minutes trying to take out my frustration on the tennis trainer but that just makes matters worse, because it shows to me what an absolute cripple I am. I just can't move quick enough and it annoys me more than anything else. I am a bundle of fun this morning! What marvellous company I am going to make. I have an iron fist around my heart squeezing, preventing anything going in or coming out. The fingers of that fist will have to be prized away one at a time and when they have gone I will be naked, free to do the Lord's will. How long will it take? Years I would think. I must just have faith in the fact that he will do it all for me, I can't and must not do anything.

Jamie's blackbird, which was sitting on the woodshed roof, has completely disappeared. We are leaving it to its own devices with the pathetic hope that it will fly back into captivity in the kitchen; the bird is called Turdus, after its Linnaen name Turdus (Merula, Merula). Quite a good name really. M. has just found Turdus and is going to try to lure him in – what a hope – from a tree in the wood.

Just been talking to Turdus, he seems very happy in his tree. I have a nasty feeling that he is being stalked by the cat – survival of the fittest, I would never have done very well if that had been the case. Clapped out a long time ago. Maybe it would have been for the best, because now that I have survived, my children will have a great chance of getting whatever I had. I wonder if I will always have it, or if it will go away as I grow. I hope so, because it really limits one's field of movement. It means that I can't up sticks and go to America, or go for a long holiday. I always have to be within a week of Canterbury which is pretty limiting, but never mind.

To kill time I am now off for a little afternoon's drive which should be fun.

Friday, July 30th
I still feel absolutely without energy, I want to do things, but I can't summon up the energy to do them. All I can do is think about them, I have no desire to do anything – let's hope this feeling wears off. All I can do is sit and look at things. I don't count writing this. Something I must do is read my Old Testament or when I come to do it tonight I will be much too tired and it will be a chore instead of a pleasure, which is what it should be. . .

80

The Old Testament was well worth reading; all about Jehu sorting out Jezebel and all the sons of Ahab — very stirring, gory stuff. The seventy sons of Ahab were all slain and their heads were sent in baskets to Jerusalem where they were divided into two piles. That was just one of Jehu's little stunts.

My knees aren't right yet, they still hurt. If I was fully active, which I have forgotten what it is like to be, I would be seeing friends, working, going to the beach, going for a holiday, there would be no end of things that I could be getting up to. I just can't wait to be better, but I must. I can't bear the thought of coming back to this stage again. Times does drag, I haven't been up for a week yet, but it feels like two, since I was ill. I have a feeling that this is about all I will be able to write to-day.

I have just been for a drive with J. to pass some time in the afternoon as is my custom. We went quite far and had quite fun getting lost in the lanes around. The accelerator return spring also broke, which is quite exciting because I suddenly found that there was terrific roar from the engine, and no play in the accelerator. I was at a loss for things or ideas of how to repair it. I tried sellotape even, and I was getting to the stage where I was having visions of being towed back by Pa, walking or pushing the car, when I saw a broken spring under Jamie's seat. With that straightened out we managed to return home. I presume tomorrow I will have to get it repaired if I want to maintain my mobility.

I have come to the conclusion that this was originally meant to be a Spiritual Journal, but owing to my lack of spirituality, has degenerated from that high level to a common diary of events. Let's hope that I maintain some of the original intention in this book. Unfortunately at present I am travelling through a dry period, so very little will be forthcoming of the spiritual nature. I wish it could though, because a lack of it just shows up the weakness of myself. Something which I need to be shown, so that I can put myself entirely in His care but something that I don't want to be shown.

Sunday, August 1st
This morning the clouds were heavy with rain, and it was dull outside, so Antoine and I decided to go for a row on the Medway at Maidstone. It was great fun and beautiful; the river was wide and deep and the trees hung quietly over, offering shade and shelter. It is surprising the quiet places one finds in the middle of the noise and industry of a town. It is very strange we have been out since ten this morning and it is now half past one and yet it seems as if I have hardly been away at all. The morning has left no impression on me. If only I could see the beauty and greatness of the Lord's work in everything, then everything would be a wonder to me, which is what it should be. We shouldn't take everything as we do, as I do I know. I have been writing this journal now for eight days, it seems like years since I wrote the first words. They were written a long time ago by somebody completely different. It is strange how I have changed in the space of such a short time.

Monday, August 2nd
Last night wasn't much fun. My knees were hurting, and I managed to work myself into a state of fear, because I thought they were going to go bad again on me. It was really very foolish; it is extraordinary how things can get so very, very important at night. I had no need to worry at all. When I prayed that they should be all right and thought on Jesus Christ, a marvellous feeling of peace came over me and I knew that all would be all right. Then I prayed for sleep by thanking God for it and it came, and all was well in the morning.

Wednesday, August 4th

Last night I went to the pub with P., Elizabeth and Antoine, and my knees started really hurting badly – came home and went to bed when everything sorted itself out fine, but I had a bit of a fight to be allowed up this morning.

Thursday, August 5th

This morning we went to Charing to Communion and found that there wasn't a service at all. We had a pleasant time meandering around the church, which was big, grey and silent. The presence of God was very much there, even though we didn't worship. Life is passing me by slowly but I am loving it, loving the beauty, the wildness and the company. God is very good to me, he has given me far more than I deserve. I deserve nothing, he has done it and will do it all for me. What have I done to warrant such love and affection?

Friday, August 6th

Yesterday was a great day, I learnt a lot about the love of God by being with Angela. It was like a spiritual recharge for which I am most grateful, I needed it. It is worth going through days and days of dryness just to be allowed these glorious respites which give one courage and faith to carry on. They show you that you are there or here for a purpose. The purpose may not be clear at the moment, but these times give you faith to wait, which is what I must do, and can do with the aid of God.

It is sad how beautiful thoughts can lose their shine by imparting them to others; sometimes you feel you have got to tell someone about them and when the telling is done, the thought, the feeling, is lost and tarnished. I have written enough for today. I will just say that God is teaching me to love him. Our Father ... These words prove it to me. I know he loves me. Why?

Saturday, August 7th

Beautiful windy, cloudy day, rather like the sort of pictures that Constable used to paint. The wild white clover is going to be harvested today. Last night had a night out with Tom who seemed to be in good form. It was lovely to be in a field which was being harvested. The smell, the dust, it was very pleasant, there is something unique about harvest which I can't describe, but is very much a part of me. I don't think I will ever be able to leave the country with all that it means to me.

Sunday, August 8th

It is so much easier when things are beautiful and silent outside to turn one's thoughts towards God. Outside it is crystal clear blue and yet gold; everything is worshipping God, the birds with song, the cows with hollering, the trees with rustling, and I am trying too. God, help me to love You and worship You in the beauty and reverence of each day.

Monday, August 9th

What is to be done today I just don't know, but if I don't think or worry about it something will crop up. I have been kept from being bored these last two weeks, so why should it not continue. I very much enjoy my morning writing and reading sessions; I find them particularly soothing. I came in here feeling a little fed up and unhappy, and leave feeling content and satisfied.

I wonder whether anyone else will read this Journal. I pity them if they do.

Tuesday, August 10th

A. and M. have gone to the dentist's — they are very brave. I couldn't force myself for anything, the very thought makes me feel nervous, and yet the two windiest members of the family have screwed themselves up to go.

God was good to me last night; won't say how, he just showed himself in action in ways that I didn't expect.

Wednesday, August 11th
A very fine windy day. The day started off well with communion which was very pleasant as it always seems to be these days.

Thursday, August 12th
Woke up this morning in little bit of pain. I was ill again. Why I don't know; I had done nothing strenuous at all. Never mind, my illness must be put to good use. I spent most of the day asleep. When I awoke I didn't know whether it was morning or evening.

Friday, August 13th
Woke up this morning still feeling pretty groggy – pain less. My *bottom lip has gone numb for some reason best known to itself and it feels like I have a necklace of lead shot hanging round it.

Saturday, August 14th
It is very difficult to find time to read and write these last couple of days because I have been so sleepy; all I can do is write or read a few lines then my eyes seem to go on strike and seize up.

I wrote the following poem a few days ago and forgot to copy it in, so here in the midst of this day's ramblings it may prove a little out of context, but never mind, the thing is to get it down:

> Of things of greater or lesser report I do not care
> Trival things seem to stand and stare one in the face
> and frighten
> While things of great import seem to drift away.

* The feeling in his lip never came back.

Lord come to me and help me,
And show that all is well between me and thee.
What is it that makes the birds sing?
What is it that makes the collared dove?
I know, Oh Lord, it is all wrapped up in your love,
I know it, Oh Lord, by instinct, as the lamb knows
how to suck,
And somewhere deep inside
Afraid to come out and yet afraid to hide
Is the little questioning voice saying 'Why?'

Sunday, August 15th
I must first say that Elizabeth Goudge's book *St. Francis
of Assisi* is simply beautiful. Like some books about Saints
it doesn't suffer from, for me, too much sentimentality,
but who am I to complain about these beautiful people
who set such an example of love and courage to us useless
paupers in spirit. With the Holy Spirit I know I can do
anything, but do I want to let him do anything? It is all
very difficult but he will do it all if I only have the courage
to let him. What must I do to help him to help me? He is
me, therefore he doesn't need my help, I must just let
myself open to his influx of love and kindness which
washes over me every now and again, leaving me happy
and fulfilled.

> The Cross hath lifted,
> Love, Heaven gifted,
> Never to let it go,
> And the Cross shall take me,
> Lift me, break me,
> For all the world to know

Jacopone da Todi

A gem of poetry, shining with love, devotion, sacrifice,
everything; the love in it seems to distil inside me into a
suppressed feeling of excitement and love.
Praying tonight I suddenly realised how obnoxious the

word 'me' was. I was saying it over and over again in a spiel of thoughtless self-remorsing words, if that is possible; there was no love there, and I knew it. I broke into the balmy relief of Our Father, what relief from the purgatory of my self-inflicted self-love. I know I shouldn't write that, but I have – let's say my prayers started off in a disgusting way and finished up by being something beautiful to me.

Monday, August 16th

I can think of nothing to say except I am enjoying everything that is being given to me in this life.

It is lovely lying here in bed with the front door and window open with all the wealth of summer smells and feelings pouring over me, embalming me in their delicate dewy softness.

Tuesday, August 17th

Another beautiful day; hot sun and cloudless sky with a gentle heat haze over everything.

I still have this pain in my jaw, but it is for Christ now, I have dedicated it to him, so that he can bring good out of it. Pain is evil, but the good that comes out of suffering is of Christ; he can always bring good out of evil.

Father Andrew's book on the *Adventure of Prayer* helped me a great deal. He is a very clear minded man who understands easily the many problems of others. I was having problems; I was thinking too much about *me*; I was praying selfishly not thinking how glorious he was or how I adore him, but I was entirely concerned with myself. Think of him. As I was told once by an Inner Voice, 'Think on my Presence.' If one does that, all else is fine and beautiful and falls into place. If you love the Lord your God with all your heart and soul, you love everything, because everything is of God, is God.

Wednesday, August 18th

Unfortunately in the night it rained and at present it is windy and overcast, so the clover harvest doesn't look like too much of a good thing.

At present I am reading a book called *Against all Reason*, about monasteries and religious orders. It certainly makes me think a lot. What am I to do for God in my short life? I am here and I am his, yet I don't know what I am to do. I know he will let me know, but it is the waiting that worries me. By going back to Wye am I doing the right thing, when I have the opportunity to chuck it? I must just leave it to him.

Thursday, August 19th

It is a lovely misty, hot morning this morning with promise of good weather for baling, and bale-carting.

The wasps are here in real earnest now. The season has opened as far as they are concerned, they are humming round the room looking for food on the back of books, under chairs, anywhere.

Friday, August 20th

The fine weather has broken, with rain and thunder. The bales so hastily made yesterday, lie around in the fields like sponges soaking up as much of the moisture as possible. Never mind. I have tiny little Willow (a kitten) sitting on me. She is so helpful when it comes to writing, the way the black letters come out of the nib of the pen absolutely fascinates her, and she has to bite, suck and paw them. She has been with us for about a week now, much to Swanley's (tomcat) disgust, poor fellow.

Sunday, August 22nd

We went to early service this morning which was most enlivening. I always return from Communion with a feeling of joy and happiness. If I tried to pin down that joy I know I would be unable to. I found also at this particular service that my thoughts weren't with my words, which is rather sad, but the fact that I uttered them is important I think, and the reward for saying them was in the joy felt at the end. Then I realized that the words that I had said had been worthwhile.

P.'s back is slightly better this morning. He is enjoying Elizabeth Goudge's book on *St. Francis of Assisi,* and I, today, have to go and fetch, or rather buy, him another book on the same subject from Hollingbourne, which ought to pass the time. It is terrible I have lost all urge to travel. A few weeks ago I would have been off like a shot, but today and all other days, I seem to be beset by this terrible lethargy, which wants me just to sit down and vegetate like a cabbage or brussel sprout. A very unpleasant feeling, but one that can be overcome by action and decision. The decision seems to be the most difficult part.

Wednesday, August 25th

This morning started with a bang, a beautiful day when I drew the curtains, but it wasn't to last more than five minutes because the bullocks had got out and were tearing around the countryside like a herd of wild rhinoceri. I never thought that we would see them again owing to the way they set off, cross country, as though they were determined to go off on holiday to Pluckley or Ashford. P.'s back is much worse today and he can't even move up off the bed to turn over, or sit up. He is going to have to learn to be patient. Last night he was champing at the bit and saying that he was going to get up and all that sort of nonsense. M. got very little sleep indeed, and is now making up for lost time. She ought by now to be a fully qualified nurse with all the work she has been doing for P. and me. I must be very very careful over the next few days while P. is as he is, because with Angela away, two invalids would be too much.

I have just said my prayers, how relaxing and comforting it is to pray. The feeling of peace is profound and pleasant and in some way it seems to round off the day so well. I know that is wrong, but it seems so right to pray and thank God for the pleasantness and enjoyment of the day. If only I could see Him in all I do and not take the purely selfish attitude that I have, of enjoying everything for the pleasure it gives me and that only. In fact how unpleasant it is living from moment to moment, getting personal satisfaction from the purely material things of life, but I presume that greater spirituality and understanding come with time and cannot be rushed. One can't expect to become perfect ever, let alone in a couple of months.

I will finish off this day by saying that P.'s little old back is much better.

Thursday, August 26th

A dull overcast day for the start of Angela's and Helena's holiday in the Lakes. Now they have gone, life really looks as though it could be dull, but we must make the most of it, taking things as we find them, then boredom won't set in too fast, I hope. It makes a great deal of difference having them around. Someone with whom one can talk, and share one's troubles, but I am on my own now and must do my best. I wonder what will happen to this little Journal when I go back to Wye?

Friday, August 27th

Had a marvellous time last night but unfortunately I have overdone it once more and my right knee is giving me trouble. It has no excuse really to do so at all; I did nothing that it could complain about fairly, like lifting sacks, or playing football. I do hope that it gets better because it is so limiting when one can do hardly anything at all without fear of reprisals from one's body. Here I am now, lying in bed, a picture of pain. It is dedicated to God for good — may good come through it.

Sunday, August 29th

Clapped out yet again, but I pray for a short time only; so wretched that I didn't write a word yesterday. P. with his bad back, in all his foolishness has walked downstairs. I wonder if he will make it up again. *The door has slammed – he has made it all right.

Monday, August 30th

All I can do at present is sleep, even though I woke up at half past ten. There seems very little to say this morning except that in general I feel better, but my right (writing) arm feels much more clapped out than it did yesterday for some reason. Yesterday I slept solidly through the whole day, and when I awoke I was sad to find that it was eight thirty in the evening as opposed to the morning, because I hoped to get on with a very good novel that I am reading. Now that I have lost all my inquisitive female readers, except for Willow, who insists on attacking the tip of my pen, I may now get on to write; what, I haven't a clue, but I just feel that I ought to be able to write something.

At present I spend ninety-five percent of my time trying to stay awake, and the other five percent trying to de-glue my eyes in order to read. By the time we have partaken of the last five (or ten) percent we are back whole-heartedly into the first ninety-five. That sounds rather like a maths calculation – the question being 'how many apples did George buy with the threepence lent to him by his Granny.' This will be quite enough for today after that futile effort. As one can see that effort is all over and I must slip into that awful state of cotton wool between waking and sleeping. It is awful the feeling of lethargy that is all over me. I go to sleep so that I may be more wakeful, but when I wake I am just as sleepy as I was when I started to sleep. I am like a bad cabbage on a compost heap getting worse and worse. Lord, I apologize for my

*Very ill. The writing of this entry was almost illegible.

prayers tonight, forgive me, I was much more tired than I thought, and praying is so relaxing and yet refreshing.

Tuesday, August 31st

My own state of health is not much to write home about, not that I would have to write very far, it is better, but my right arm hurts rather a lot. I don't think I will get up until that is passed.

Wednesday, September 1st

My right arm, or hand, or whatever it is, hurts more and more. It has no reason to because I do nothing more strenuous with it than lift a teapot (and that I do with two hands), or write this journal. Last night for the first time in my life I was able to feel pity or sadness at the plight of the Pakistani War Victims, because apart from their battered and stained bodies, their bloated stomachs and their big, pleading gazelle-like frightened eyes, I could see Christ saying 'Feed me, clothe me, shelter me.' The tortured, sad body of Christ in Pakistan was pleading for help. Looking back on it, on the scenes, I realised that I was feeling something akin to love for those dear, scared people.

Last night I was reading a good book, and, as is my custom, I read my Bible and say my prayers before I read, because otherwise I am apt to fall asleep. I started out on my prayers with a slight intention of hurrying, but the dear sweet Lord would have nothing of it in his way, he gently rebuked me, I don't know how, and my prayers went on in their own sweet way. I pray to learn to love the Lord, I thank him that my prayers are being answered by degrees, just a tiniest bit of the cloth that reveals all is being lifted up, so that I can feel and experience some of the warmth and love, and from that experience it is only natural that I should want more. Nothing is ever forced, but I defy anybody who has had some slight feeling of God's love and care direct, to turn away. The whole world is a tangible example of God's love for us, and it is only our fault that there are wars and famine and starvation. Is not the world rather like a soul that has seen the Love that is offered, and is fighting against it for its worldly part. And having seen the Lord many search for him, but God is forced to break the spirit of rebellion, or to be first seen making good out of evil. Good always comes from evil if we want it. All we have to do is to pray and an unquenchable, unbeatable and unlimited supply of power for good is at our hands.

Very tired, but fully satisfied and happy. I am fully content with life; what more could I want when God is so good and beautiful to me. How have I deserved his richness; I do not know – maybe I will find out one day.

Friday, September 3rd
Not feeling so good again today. My right knee and arm are hurting quite a lot. I think half my trouble now, as I have been ill such a lot, is hypochondria. The slightest twinge and I tell M. and want injections, all unnecessary. I don't know how I can stop it. Maybe God will help me; He knows always that my pain is dedicated to him, to do good with. Writing this hurts. I am self-centred and spoilt. God will do it all for me if I only ask him, I know. There is nothing that I need do except ask for his power to be realised. It is already in me, as he is me. That is quite enough about me. If I keep on thinking about *me* (what a loathsome word) my little head will burst.

Saturday, September 4th
I feel now that it is time that I got up. I am well enough and fit enough to be able to take the rigours of the day on my pins, but unfortunately the maternal clamp is bound to come down, and I will be told that I mustn't. I, personally, don't think it makes any difference what I do; I think that if I am going to be unwell I will be, and that is all there is to it. If only they could find what is wrong, or find some cure.

I have just thought of something quite interesting to say, but unfortunately P. came in and disturbed me. Oh yes, that was it, it was about P. He has recovered from his gut trouble. We think that it was arsenic poisoning, but now his back has gone out in a different place. I hope that he has gone to lie down. He is like I used to be; he won't stop until he grinds to a halt, always trusting in providence to put the ailment right. A perfectly valid attitude. If animals have such powers of self recuperation, why can't we have them also? I reckon I am just a bad number. If normal, natural selection had taken place I would have bought it long ago. Not a very comforting thought that one is a physical failure or misfit. If they introduce selective breeding in the future, I will be a non breeder. Sad, but necessary.

Sunday, September 5th

A very pleasant day but unfortunately I don't think I will be able to write very much as my right arm seems to have seized up rather badly — something to gripe about anyway. This writing seems to be slowly loosening my arm off, one wouldn't believe it looking at the finished product, but I presume it is about as bad as usual. A very autumnal day with the bird song being made up mainly of starlings, sparrows and robins; I love the former bird in their cheeky simplicity and their frugal vulgarity — they are always happy birds.

This evening I found my prayers very difficult to say. I could feel some physical mental block against being able to contact Christ. This block is completely of my own engineering and the only way I found that I could remove it was by starting my prayers straight away with the Lord's Prayer. I found in all else I was looking for something that wasn't there. I feel that I was looking, even expecting a spiritual experience. I have found that nearly every night my prayers are a spiritual experience of a kind, a sort of rest in God is the best way to describe them, and

I have usually found if one sets out in the worst frame of mind, by the end of my prayers I feel rested in God. But this is something that one should not expect every time as quickly as I usually attain it, but it was mine eventually this evening. I won't say mine because the victory was entirely his; He conquered whatever it was in me that was keeping us so tangibly apart.

Monday, September 6th

This morning I have yet again that general feeling of dissatisfaction at my present condition, feeling that my stay in bed is entirely due to my own weakness, and is not really necessary at all. I feel in many ways that I am enjoying my stay in bed to such an extent that I am playing a part to keep myself here, but there is no doubt that I am in a little discomfort and when I get up it gets worse, but I feel that it is crazy staying in bed because I have a sore arm. Never mind — the less I think about myself the better. At the moment I am a little bit desolate because I have just finished a very good book. It always leaves a hole behind, and unless one is very quick in the filling of it, the hole can turn into lethargy and boredom.

Tuesday, September 7th

I have got up nice and early today but I really don't know why, or what I am to do except read, which I am beginning to find rather dull work. I must admit though that I am much more satisfied with this Journal than I thought would be possible. It is a constant source of worry to me that it will finish. I presume that is the best way of keeping it going; turning it into a pleasant duty, which it is and isn't. It isn't a duty but it is pleasant. There is a curious smell entering the room; I wonder whether it is the pigs, or if it is the kitten. I hope very strongly that it is the former, as the kitten, much to his discomfort, has got the most abominably loose insides. The underneath of my bed is free from all traces of anything unpleasant I am pleased to say – no bogey men or anything else, only paper and a pair of pants. It must be pigs.

Wednesday, September 8th
A glorious start to the day, the sky is absolutely clear blue and the sun is shining, but a glorious start to a day with very little prospects at all. I have nothing to do except write dull letters to insurance companies, etc. How I hate business letters, but how little actual trouble they are when one gets down to them. It is the continued putting off that makes them so unpleasant. Poor P. has gone back to school today as stiff as a board; I wonder how he will be when he comes back. I know he enjoys it. I wonder what work I will do; I know my life ought to de dedicated to the service of others, but how am I with my very few attributes to set about doing that? I find it difficult enough as it is without making a career of it. I presume I could do a job which one doesn't normally connect with the service of others, but by my way of life turn it to the use of others. Anyway I will find out eventually.

This morning my whole life is being plagued by inquisitive wasps; they come flying around with that sickening noise of theirs and dive bomb me, and whatever I do seems to make them more keen and excited. They are foul creatures, but they have their duty to perform. I wish they wouldn't do it around me. It may be that they are just friendly and want to pay their respects, but I feel that I can do very well without them.

Thursday, September 9th
Today the house drains itself of people. P. is back at school and Jamie and Helena both return to theirs. Thank heavens I have finished all that foolishness even though I am carrying on at university; the difference is as great as chalk from cheese. I would never willingly go back and do all that palaver again; it was useful in its way, but petty to a great degree.

Saturday, September 11th
The house has emptied itself of yet more people, it gets ominously quieter and quieter. One thing that must not happen is for me to go to bed when everybody has gone. I must not, in fact, get ill again and must have it out with the doctors why I constantly get ill. The whole thing makes very little sense to me at all. I must be in Wye for the first days of the term or I will never be able to hold my head up again. I have a reputation for being an invalid which I hope to dispel . . .

Sunday, September 12th
Last night I had a new visitor in the shape of the kitten. A much lighter companion than that enormous panther that comes in every now and again. Today I am going over to see Tom. I must take things very gently, get back early; I simply refuse to go ill again. I think it would drive me mad. I think I have been ill about fourteen times since last October, which must be somewhere approaching a world record.
    Heigh-ho away, for another day.

Monday, September 13th
Last night I was really let off the hook for a change; my back was hurting somewhat and I couldn't get to sleep, and I had visions of being ill once again, but fortunately M. gave me some pills and everything was fine when I woke up this morning. The house really is empty now, only M. and I, but I don't feel that I am going to be bored, which is what I usually feel when I am so starved of company. That's not very complimentary to M., who is very fine company indeed, but it is the lack of variation which I find a trifle dull and after Friday it is going to be like that the whole time until I go back to Wye, if I do. Yesterday, I went over and saw Tom and we picked up C. – them two really are marvellous company. I honestly quite fancy C. who is both attractive and pleasant, really a

very nice girl.

This book has really deteriorated from a Journal with spiritual leanings, to jottings about my very, at present, wasted love life. Let's hope they both make good reading in twenty years time. The spiritual side has been very much absent now for about two or three weeks, but it is something one can't force and something one doesn't want to force. I must just wait until I am through this period – I know it will come to an end.

Tuesday, September 14th

Wye College rang up today to say that a medical certificate of fitness was a condition of readmission. The chances of me obtaining one are absolutely nil as far as I can see. This is what I have been fearing for a long time. In a way I feel relieved that things have come to a head at last, and it will give me a breathing space and time to reconsider my life. I am absolutely useless for anything now. What good are all my A levels, they won't get me any place at all? They won't get me a career. At the moment I am stuck high and dry with no place to go and nothing to do. I can't go anywhere anyway, because I am tied to my doctors. What's the betting that as soon as the College goes back I am as fit as a flea, and don't have any more trouble at all. It is just the sort of thing that happens. If I could get Physics 'A' Level it would be marvellous; then I could be a vet or doctor. I want a career with a solid base underneath me. Life really is proving a trifle dodgy at the moment; let's just pray that things sort themselves out a bit. The thought of spending yet another year at home is a bit overpowering, but never mind, with the help of Christ anything is possible to one who has faith. Maybe this is all intended; I don't know, but we will soon find out. If I am just patient and have faith all will be all right, and the thing he wants me to do will be what I want to do above all else in the world. There – I have got rid of most of my worries; there is still a tiny ray of hope in the form of Dr. Donald, but I won't pin much hope there.

Wednesday, September 15th
I have been clapped out again; my back, bottom and neck really hurt. That's all I am writing today, let's hope it clears up soon.

Thursday, September 16th
I have been asleep solidly for the last twenty four hours or so, or at least incapable of sensible thought for that amount of time.

Friday, Sepotember 17th
Fully recovered now with no cause for complaint at all, and I intend to get up before lunch if that is allowed by the Management, which I am sure it won't be — we'll fight against it all the same! It is interesting that one can tell one's progress of recovery by the clarity of the writing. The day before yesterday it was terrible. Yesterday it wasn't too bad and today it is fine, so I reckon that means I am one hundred per cent O.K. and should be allowed up any time now.

I have just started to read Thomas Merton's *Seeds of Contemplation*. Whenever I read anything I feel I have to write about it; it may just be selfish sentimentality but when I read anything I feel peace and a flowing of satisfaction inside.

Saturday, September 18th
This morning I started off by reading straight away, having forgotten about my Journal. Angela has sadly gone off to Oxford again; I don't mean she is sad but I am, she is so good and kind and such good company. That's my epitaph to Angela until I see her again which I hope will be very soon.

Now that I have got a year to kill, I could type my Journal out to pass the time. I had final instructions this morning from Wye that they couldn't have me back — sad but inevitable. I don't mind as much as I thought I would. The thing I regret most is the fact that I will lose all my friends. It is extraordinary how quickly one loses them if one isn't in constant contact.

I must see if I can keep some of the old channels open, especially to some of the more important friends. When I say important I mean important to me personally only, and in no other way, but it is difficult keeping tabs on them even sometimes as I have found to my cost in the past. But I don't intend to go into all my intimate friendships at College, not for anyone. I am just sad, very sad that I will be leaving them. Never mind, life is full of extraordinary twists which usually work out for one's own benefit. That's the way it has worked for me so far and I hope it keeps up its old friendly style of operation.

Now I must get up because writing in this strain is making me thoroughly sorry for myself. Actually in a way maybe it is quite a good, gentle way of breaking the inevitable news to myself, without anyone, or anything, giving me a nasty surprise. I do hope I am well during the next year, I sure am fed up to the back teeth with being ill, and this coming year could be such a marvellous opportunity in which to do things that I have wanted to. If only I could throw off the shackles of my illness then all would be well and I could lead a normal life which is what, at the moment, I desperately want. But if this is to be my lot, which I pray it isn't, I must accept it and make good come out of it.

I am more depressed now and thinking how depressed I am makes me even more depressed. It is a vicious circle which if one felt enough, and enough times, one will either dissolve into tears, get into a furious temper, or have a nervous breakdown. I am now applying the brakes to my giddy goings on so none of the latter occurs, and I will either get up or write about something completely different.

When I see something truly beautiful I wish that I could think of God straight away, but unfortunately I cannot, I can only think of the pleasure that it gives to me individually. I presume that life will change me slowly, make me think of other people more than myself. That was one thing the book of Job did for me. For a short while I was able to think of his and other people's suffering, brought on them through no fault of their own, but by fate. C.S. Lewis suggests that pain is a method used by God to bring people to Him. I don't believe this, I think all pain and suffering is the work of the devil, and God brings from it Good; but I don't know, I am about as theologically endowed as a dungheap. I can think about things, but I have an awful feeling that the answers I come up with could be so wrong. This, I think, is the danger of theology; one person can affect the spiritual life of millions. It takes a very brave or gifted man, I think, to take such a step – I am neither.

Monday, September 20th

Yesterday in my rashness, I read through some of this book. The same things kept on recurring over and over again, complaints and falsities. Everything appears to me to be a bit larger than life, or a bit more grim. Last night for the Old Testament reading we read Job, which I think is really wonderful; in fact there is no word to describe the literary beauty of it, or the spiritual common-sense of it. I am going to write a little piece of it out in this book, because last night as I was reading it, I thought, for some reason, it was me speaking, not Job. I haven't looked at the piece this morning. I hope it is applicable or it might just be me over-dramatising, as usual. Looking at it this morning I think it applies to people who really suffer, not to me:

Why should the Sufferer be born to see the light?
Why is life given to men who find it so bitter?
They wait for death, but it does not come,
They seek it more eagerly than hidden treasures,
They are glad when they reach the tomb,
And when they come to the grave they exult,
Why should a man be born to wander blindly by,
Hedged in by God on every side?
My sighing is all my food,
And groans pour from me in a torrent,
Every terror that haunted me has caught up with me,

All that I feared has come upon me,
There is no peace of mind or quiet for me;
I chafe in torment and have no rest.

Poor Job, how he needs help and comfort. In many ways he is the battered, beaten body of Christ on earth today. He is the suffering refugee, living in a pipe in India. He is a thalidomide child in a wheel chair, a mongol child or a blind man. Job to me is the personification of all suffering on earth, not just physical. He is the man who has lost his family in a car accident, or a farmer whose farm has been burnt to the ground. It may be that the book of Job is a prophecy of the suffering that Christ would have to undergo when he came down to earth. I haven't yet read part of the first piece of advice given by his 'friends', so I can say no more. All I can say is that practical help is much better than advice or wise council. So saying, I start on the last page of my book, having thoroughly enjoyed writing and thinking about Job. I think maybe the spiritual side of this Journal has been saved from the fire in the last gasping passages. I will never know; someone may, someone who is fool enough to try and read it.

Tuesday, September 21st
Yesterday I finished off the story of Job and I am glad to say that his high-faluting, advising friends got told off, in

the end, by the Lord for not putting his case correctly, which I think was very fair, and Job got all his money, land and wealth back. Not that I think a man like that would really worry about such things. What really upset Job was, I think, the loss of contact with his God, the feeling of being utterly despised and rejected by the one whom he thought was his greatest friend and comforter.

There is a lot in Job, I think that it is the best book in the Old Testament, maybe because I delight in the beauty of the English, but also I am sure it has a very profound lesson for modern humanity. Anyway, it made me do something for the Charities I *say* I am always going to do things for. Practical assistance is always so much better than a lot of self-righteousness and hot air.

The only reason I am, at the moment, lying down on my bed writing is that I have nothing else to do at all. By the end of a year of it I should know if I am a writer or just a part-time hack, a scribbler who has nothing else to do. I am afraid to say I feel unfortunately like the latter. The only way I don't measure up to a hack, in my mind, is that I don't have an old raincoat, a beard and T.B. – these, I feel, are all part of the hack's make up; maybe I will acquire them all later on in life, when I have left home and am destitute in a wet slum-dwelling the docklands.

As I keep on saying, this passes the time and as I will be the only person bored, why worry? The answer is that I have a feeling that someone else will read this, and I think that it is sad that they should be bored. If only I had the ability of light humourous writing, but unfortunately I haven't, so my unfortunate clandestine reader, you will continue to be bored. Actually you may find what I find boring amusing; if such is the case you could have a very amusing time.

This could be called 'The Thoughts of a Twentieth-century Hypochondriac', or 'Time Wasting as a Hobby', anything would do except possibly 'Train Spotters' Almanack 1899'. Now seriously I would think that this sort of thing hasn't been done before — why? The reasons are very obvious because it is a complete and utter waste of time, and that is why I do it.

My trouble is as soon as I start to read my Bible, or a Spiritual book, or say my prayers I begin to feel tired, so I say to myself, right, you will say your prayers first as they are the most important part of your life; then you can do all your reading. But by the time I have read my Bible I am too tired to do anything else. The obvious answer is that I must set time aside during the middle of the day, say after lunch, when I can read a spiritual book. A very good intention, but will I keep it? Well, I have written this book every day for a couple of months so I should be able to do that little thing, and I hope it will be an intrinsic, pleasurable part of my day. Having said that I can honestly say that inside I feel better, but still feel a great need of spiritual reading; it is like an unfilled want inside — as bad as wanting a glass of water on a hot day.

Wednesday, Sepotember 22nd
The pain down the right side of my arm is beginning to be more persistent, also my leg is a little uncomfortable. Do you know I am such a hypochondriac that I reckon I could think myself into bed. We shall see; if only I have the courage to think, as it were, in the other way, but I am afraid to say I gave that up as a futile task many months ago. I must just say that my arm is stiff this morning after all that writing yesterday, so using the old worn-out yesterday phrase, I am a hack with only half an arm to stand on. I am sorry to say that sounds rather pathetic today — yesterday I thought it quite amusing. I will battle manfully on hoping against hope for inspiration from somewhere. It has arrived; we are off to communion this minute, so I have to think no more. All I have to do is shut my pen and book and shuffle off.

I have returned now and feel completely better, not an

ache, pain or doubt; such is the power of Christ. The more I think about it, the more miraculous my cure becomes. I really was feeling lousy before church; now I feel as fresh as a daisy and think I might even go as far as to walk down the yard.

I have done my reading and thoroughly enjoyed it. One thing that particularly caught me was this:

> If you write for God you will reach many men
> and bring them joy.
> If you write for men you may make some money,
> and you may give someone a little joy, and you
> may make a noise in the world for a little while.
> If you write for yourself you can read what you
> yourself have written, and after ten minutes you
> will be so disgusted you will wish you were dead.
>
> *Thomas Merton*

I hate to think where I stand. I have always said that this book is for my eyes only, but I don't find it disgusting, yet I never set out with the intention of writing for God or man. Well I have established it is not for myself; the original idea was a Spiritual Journal inspired by Thomas Merton's Journal. Maybe what has happened is that it was originally intended for God, but owing to my lack of spirituality, it has descended to wavering between something written for men and myself. I have let myself off the hook rather easily, but how could someone like me write for God? I presume that, like I give my pain to Christ when I am ill, so that he can bring good out of evil, I could give this to God, so that he can reach many men and bring them joy. His all binding love could reach out and join many. I doubt, but all things are possible to God. The trouble is that anything I write now is so insignificant and unimportant. It did not worry me in the least before, but now every word has assumed frightening importance. I intend to keep on in the same way; if God intends to use this, he will. This may seem an extremely immature attitude, and it may be so, but it is all that I can do at present.

A very sad thing has happened; Turdus has disappeared, he has been gone since half past eight and hasn't returned. I don't hold out much hope for him I am afraid — all we can do is search and pray.

Thursday, September 23rd
This morning it is very grey and overcast and all the bullocks are lying down thinking of rain. The sound of anything travels much farther than usual and one can hear tractors and diggers working miles away. I think I feel so active because the air this morning seems to be particularly stimulating — it is the sort of day I would like to be working on a tractor or chasing cows — some form of manual work, anyway.

Yesterday I lifted a one hundred and four pound gas cylinder on to a lorry without suffering any defects which I thought was rather marvellous. I have been evicted from my bed by a cat which is by me right under the pillows and I don't have the heart to turf her off. She looks so comfortable curled up there fast asleep. It would take a very heartless person to shift her.

As I intend to go out this afternoon I must do my Spiritual reading earlier than normal. I learnt a lot yesterday in one way and another; let's hope that today is just as successful.

I have completed my spiritual reading for today and it was time well spent. Thomas Merton really was an extraordinarily holy man. What he writes proves how deeply involved in the love of God he is. The things that he writes about just wouldn't occur to me, but I wouldn't expect them to anyway. I don't say that despairingly or with regret; I say it with joy that the love of God should have found such a clean, pure channel as that man, and I hope that as I develop in the christian faith, the love of God may be able to use me as such a channel in anyway that he pleases.

Friday, September 24th
A beautiful foggy wraith-like morning, with all the starlings making autumnal noises. Winter is coming quickly this year for some reason; perhaps it is because I pay more attention to the changes in the weather than I used to. The weather affects the countryside so much that I can't understand why I didn't notice it more often in days gone by. Today I am going to spend over at Tom's so I have no worries about heavy time and boredom. M. was honestly planning to take me over there and fetch me back, what next! Talk about being tied to apron strings, it is just too ridiculous, but she said it because she was worried about me, so I have no reason at all to complain. How many people's mothers are that concerned? Most of them are too pleased by half to get them off their hands whenever they can.

I feel I have to write some more because I had such a joyous day, looking back on it, but the actual time spent wasn't particularly joyful because I was always bugged with the worry was I overdoing it? Would others have to pay for my present enjoyment? I think I have got away with it, but presume only time will tell. The trouble with my illness is that I don't know I am ill until the morning after, but I feel so well now that I don't think I could be ill. All I can do is hope and pray; I must admit that I feel very tired – it's been a long day and I am glad that M. has forced me into bed at this early hour. I have still to do my daily reading.

I have been reading *Seeds of Contemplation*. It makes me realise how little I know and understand, and makes me ask the question will I ever fully comprehend? I am so weak, so attached to the worldly ways, is there any hope that God will be able to work through me? In the book Merton touches on every point concerning prayer and meditation and contemplation, showing me up for what I am in every case, showing me how long the road is that I have to travel. If only I could see God in everything, in every person and action instead of shutting up my spiritual activities into special times. Time to read a book, time to read my Bible and say my prayers. No! This is all wrong. One's whole life should be one God-wards movement. The pure seeking of the longing to do his will every minute of every day. The channelling of his love and Spirit through to other people so they benefit and return his love. I just pray that this were all possible to me.

To love God I found months ago difficult; how could I love God? This used not to worry me, but it used to bother me. I prayed that I could have the ability to love God. Slowly over the days there has built up in me a feeling that I did love God, but a feeling is just an inner emotion that can be turned on and off at will, and has to be guarded against. Emotions are no good except, possibly, for one feeling I have had which happened on just two or three occasions when I probably needed it most.

These were feelings of infinite beauty and solitude, of blue and crystal purity, feelings of being loved and cared for, and I have never forgotten them. But to get back; Now I don't feel that I love God, I know I love him. My love is difficult to describe, except at the moment I want to shout about it, laugh about it, cry about it and tell the world about it. It is best summed up in the words 'Our Father'. To say these words, draws me to him and to the whole world. He is our Father, and we are his children, and he cares intensely for everyone of us and it is our job to look after each other, as brother and sister in any family would.

How I long to be able just to lie here and write continuously about God – His love and mystery – it is the most gloriously rewarding way of passing the time. In these last words are summed up to me why I can't and it is a very good thing that I am unable to do so. First because one can become over attached to spout one's own theories when they may be completely wrong; and secondly it is not a subject one takes up to pass the time. Now I am completely dry inside, having said all that, and so no more can be expected tonight. I don't want to stop – maybe I am becoming too fond of the sound of my own pen.

Sunday, September 26th
Last night I had an uncomfortable feeling in my back. I am now writing at five past eleven at night. Even though I did go over and see Tom today we did very little indeed except sit around; even that made me feel ill and clapped out. I am sure half my illness is my mind, but I don't want to talk about that, it makes me feel uncomfortable; it is a load of twaddle that it is in the mind. A pain is a pain, full stop. I feel much better now than I did this afternoon which is a relief. I don't really know what else to say except that I want very much to go on writing; it is a great pleasure and gives me a strange sort of satisfaction.

I have a cat on the bottom of the bed; it is wonderful the comfort, warmth and cleanliness they seem to exude.

I am sorry this is so dull. It can give no one any pleasure, this talking about feelings and objects that no one has ever seen or can understand; but bear with me, it is helping me greatly having you there, my friendly imaginary audience. I don't mean your presence, but having you to unload my bores on to; who else but you would want to know about that dear sweet cat on the end of my bed? Everyone will now be worried that I have delusions of fame and grandeur; don't worry yourselves, I couldn't care a hang about myself. This odd rambling is only a way of filling up space.

Monday, September 27th

It is only half past seven in the morning, and I have been awake since about seven – simply unable to get back to sleep, so there seemed nothing for it for me except to do a tiddly bit of writing. This will make me feel more like sleep – it gums up the eyes like reading. There are now louder sounds of activity as if people were really on the move at last. It is extraordinary how a little noise can make a great difference. The whole prospect of the house has changed; people are up and about, running round thinking that they are going to be late; thank heavens that is not one of my concerns, and if I get up now there would be a good chance of company. But I am not sure I will yet. It is so comfortable lying here in the warmth of my bed writing nonsense. There, that is P. coming down from washing, having fed the pigs, and M. back from putting Helena on the bus, so I really think that now the time has come to get up.

I have made today a very long day, purely by chance, but it has been definitely a long enjoyable day. Let's hope for great things from tomorrow. I am afraid that as to that, I am a little apprehensive, but there is no need, everything will take care of itself as it always does. It is just a matter of looking forward to what tomorrow offers and accepting it at its own value; not what you personally can get out of it for yourself, but what can be done for God. One should not make the day into a personal struggle for one's own good; by doing so one will be doing battle continuously with other people, and therefore doing battle against the will of God, and Christ embodied in these people. If only I could learn my own lessons. It is so easy to lie here and come to these conclusions, but it is so difficult to put them into practice. It is natural for man to put himself first.

Tuesday, September 28th

Things are already happening today, pleasant, gentle things. For instance I have promised to stone twelve pounds of plums; pleasant but particular work.

I feel quite keen to write a turn or two more, so here I am ready for the fray with twenty four pounds of stoned plums behind my back; quite remarkable I think. What a job it turned out to be, monotonous, but somehow satisfying. Thinking of spiritual things is a strange thing, in some ways it is elusive. One knows something spiritual, many people have the same knowledge, yet one fears that by telling, the thought will tarnish; but what is the point of contemplation unless one shares it? This surely is the whole point, to share and spread the love of God to the ultimate glory of God.

J. sent some simply brilliant poems home. He has the wonderful ability to use exactly the right adjective or metaphor at the right time, giving his poems an intense beauty. I think he takes all those things in subconsciously and doesn't realise that they are there until he misses them. I find all his poems have a poignancy about them.

Perhaps I will write some more tonight, but at the moment I must go off and see how my plum jam is getting along. Having stoned twenty-four pounds I am now going to make twenty-four pounds into jam – I fear greatly for the result.

Wednesday, September 29th

Tonight prayer was very difficult. Every time I tried my mind wandered off on the most extraordinary tracks completely unforeseen and unwanted. I know that this is no sin but it is so sad that the moment I put aside for prayer should be ruined thus by every-day thoughts, cares and worries. But I must remember that Christ is there to share our worries. Our worries are his, so having them bursting

111

in like this could be more of a blessing than one thinks. They could be a gentle method of getting one out of a rut.

Jesus Christ knows his own. I don't know if these are the correct words, but all the same I find them very comforting, because it means that no person has an advantage. That doesn't mean that one should just leave everyone to get on in their own way on the assumption that people will be shown, come what may, because you may be the chosen instrument to show them, and therefore by leaving them alone one is ignoring God's will, if his will takes you that way. The driving force should be the love of spreading God's love to others. The reward being the fact that you have done something for the further glorification of God. The further glorification of God being the sharing of His love with those other people, and hence the spreading of his love. It is one marvellous, never ending circular system, with God and his love making the whole affair work.

I often worry that the thoughts and conclusions drawn by me may be untrue and totally astray. Lord forgive me if I am wrong.

Thursday, September 30th
Woke up this morning feeling pretty dodgy, but thankfully everything has settled down very comfortably and it looks as though the trouble will blow over quite quickly. This morning, spurred on by my success at plum jam making, I am going to try my luck at plum port and various other jams, such as elderberry and haw jam, just for fun. It is a good way of occupying one's time with benefits for everyone. I should think it will all be pretty disgusting but we shall see. I won't promise anything grippingly exciting for this evening.

I feel clapped out but not bad enough to go to bed. I have pains in my leg and my back which don't seem to be getting much better. I thought I had got over it but

112

apparently not. Sad if I am ill, because it means I won't see Tom before he leaves for Glasgow, but these things happen and you have to take the rough with the smooth. The latter would be just a little rough.

I am afraid I have very nearly given up all hope of recovery without a few days in bed. It is such a nuisance having to face the inevitable, but I am not quite feeling it yet — I refuse until I absolutely have to. That moment hasn't arrived, but I can see it tanking over the horizon very fast like a steam train with a grin on its face; black and menacing and very noisy. It is coming over the brow of the hill and I am trapped to the line. I will see if I can eat lunch.

I closed the book, but there is no point until Elizabeth arrives home for lunch — she seems to be taking rather a long time. Ah, that is Liz back once more; now to lunch. That last phrase is rather like the finishing of the Acts of the Apostles 'And now to Rome'.

Saturday, October 2nd
It caught up with me, or rather, the train mowed me down and mauled me. It has passed over now and I am already recovering, feeling pretty rough all the same. Sad that it had to happen now as I had various things planned for the next few days, but they as usual will have to go by the board. If this is God's method of using me, I am happy, as I will be doing his will; if it is not, I am still well pleased as God can always bring goodness out of evil.

Sunday, October 3rd
I feel completely recovered this morning — strange how quickly these things come and go. One morning really bad, and the next ready to get up and be about and doing anything. This illness, planted right here, stopped my wine-making experiments, and my seeing of Tom off to Scotland — the latter was very sad.

This morning I feel much closer to God than usual. I know that this is pure emotion and one shouldn't rely on them as staging posts or such like, and one shouldn't look for them; but they are very pleasant all the same. It is when you know something that it can be relied on. It is impossible ever to pretend to know something, however hard you try. There is no escaping the real knowledge and when you do know that something, you will wonder why you had never thought of it before.

It is an extraordinary thought, a beautiful thought, that God is in everything that we touch, do and see, because Christ is in us, and therefore in everything we touch and do. So Christ is in everything from teaspoons to toothbrushes. They are there because Christ willed it; without that will they wouldn't be there, proving that we have nothing outside Christ, without Him we are nothing, we couldn't survive – we wouldn't be here. God is our all.

I am sorry to say that I am getting myself a little bogged down. I have got the message over to myself, which I don't think I had before. Having learnt now that he is in everything, I must learn to praise and adore him in everything. It is a strange feeling being totally surrounded by God – an inexplicable feeling. I think that I must finish for the time being as my thoughts seem to be getting more and more tangled, and woollier and woollier as time goes on.

Just worked out that it was fifteen days exactly since I was last ill; I believed it to be much longer ... I feel absolutely fine until I move about, then my leg begins to hurt. This is the most annoying type of illness, as one feels fine the whole time one is in bed, and then the slightest movement causes discomfort, so one has to stay in bed feeling well which leads to all sorts of frustrated feelings and reactions, which can offend and hurt other people. One has to watch out for them.

At present I am fed up with being in bed. Anything I try and do is a drag and a waste of time. I have never felt like this before in all my illnesses. Let's hope I can get whatever it is out of my system and into the pages of this book, where it will be harmless. The trouble is, even the thought of writing fills me with a terrible lassitude, a wet feeling around the gills. I could go to sleep, but I don't want to. What is the matter? It is really making me a little desperate. It's like trying to go to sleep on an empty stomach or having 'flu on a hot day. Like being a bag of jelly – anything that is soft and floppy, I am that.

This morning I have got to remain in bed, but it is fixed that I get up for lunch, and during the afternoon I am to make all sorts of interesting things like blackberry syrup and honey ale, which ought to be relaxing and entertaining.

Helena for some reason thoroughly approves of it all; it appeals to the squirrel streak that is so prevalent in her. It is very difficult this morning because M. has chosen to iron in the drawing room, making writing jolly nearly impossible. My day started at the ludicrous hour of quarter past six, and consequently I am tired now. Swanley spent the whole night in here.

This is one thing that has worried me recently – I have been so easily rattling along talking about nothing of interest and I have been getting no Divine assistance. I am sure that the flow has been stopped from my end. The flood of light is always there, but I haven't drawn my curtains to let it in, or I have let my windows get dirty. I have a feeling that it is because I haven't read a Spiritual book for some time, since Wednesday at least. Heavens! that seems a long time ago, but it is only five days. When one thinks of days in numbers, e.g. one week equalling seven days, time is very little, but if you think of days as a series of events, thoughts and actions, time is much more profitable and longer.

Now that I have got a free year (oh woe!) this Journal has a greater chance of sticking in roots, like a parasitic verruca, and surviving. That's not very complimentary to it, but the thoughts of the free year bring to mind apparitions of verrucas, warts, and unhealthy things.

I have made the blackberry syrup and I am feeling pretty clapped-out, but clapped-out tired, not clapped-out ill; there is a subtle and real difference between the two, and I with my months of experience can tell the difference quite well. When to be worried and when not to be worried.

Looking back on my original judgement I don't know if it was quite right; there seems to be a fair old knot building up in the inside of the back of my head, but we must just hope it will pass away.

Tuesday, October 5th
This little book will have to wait a bit. I must leave for the stove which is to be my master for a little of this morning. Already the morning is nearly over. I have completed it without ill effect, and have made some elderberry syrup, which smells pretty disgusting, but people wouldn't make it if it was unpleasant. All the same there is no accounting for taste; people will eat and drink the most revolting things and apparently love them.

For some odd reason this morning I am finding that I am constantly using the wrong word in speech and in writing; this morning I wanted to ask Len how he measured a gallon of potatoes and found myself asking how he measured a gallon of blackberries. Annoying, because it means that you have to prepare every sentence; sometimes even that isn't enough to avert disaster.

I don't know if I said, but I am reading a new book by Thomas Merton (I mean new to me), called *Life and Holiness*, which is really about leading a christian life in a materialistic world. Similar in many ways to Watchman Nee's book. Two interesting things arose from Merton's book. Firstly in many ways he says what I have been

116

feeling, that good works done without the guiding of the Holy Spirit are not as good as works done with the Holy Spirit, however insignificant and unmagnificent the works may be. This is obvious, and I have put it badly. What I should have said is that the Holy Spirit and the love of God should start you inspirationally into works of love. So one has to look to oneself before others. Clean out your own back yard before you try to tend other people's. The other chapter which I enjoyed was his discourse on the sacraments. All the while I was reading it I had a bunched up feeling inside. I was frightened what I was going to find. He being a monk, I expected all sorts of things which I wouldn't be able to take, but I needn't have feared; he was writing for everyone as usual. The first time I read it I was so concerned about what I was going to read next that I took nothing in — I had to read it again.

Now I must off and make some Honey Beer!

Wednesday, October 6th
A lovely, lovely day, The sort of day which can only be produced in autumn — cold but brilliantly sunny. The whole world hums with life. The birds, bees and every creeping thing vibrate with throbbing life. Collecting, migrating or just living, but whatever it is it is very important.

If only I could find the words to describe adequately my feelings, but I am unable, I wasn't built that way. How can I describe the warmth of the sun in Pluckley Village Square, the horse trotting through and the old people ambling quietly to the library? Everything is too great for words. It's at moments like these that it should be easiest to think of God in all his glory. I try, I see the beauty of it, I know it comes from God, and is God, but I find it very difficult to think of him at these moments, because I am enjoying the pleasant effect of everything on the senses. If only I could do it all simultaneously and spontaneously, instead of retrospectively. Maybe I will soon.

117

I strained my honey beer today, which smelt very strange, and also I started the preparation of the rose syrup, which I hope won't be too revolting. It couldn't be as revolting as the elderberry, of which the very thought makes me feel sick.

Thursday, October 7th

Today, believe it or not, is a very important, notable, thoroughly memorable day. Today, twenty years ago, the world stood hushed and waited with baited breath. Then the great event took place, the event which was to revolutionise my life, to change me entirely, and to affect me catastrophically for the remainder of my years on this planet – I was born. Yes, my dear clandestine audience, today is my birthday, but today there are to be no celebrations, no fun feastings, and gaiety. Today the bells have to keep their peace, and the cannons must remain silent, because it is inconvenient. I have got to pretend that I was born on this coming Saturday. How does one do that? Is it entirely possible? I must try. There, I have blown my trumpet enough, the echoes are just dying away. I had to, as no one else would, because this really was the day whatever anyone says. Apart from all my caluddle about the day I am very glad it is to be on Saturday, as the others will be at home and it will be much more fun.

What to do today is the great question? What is to be done and how can I best do it? when? where? what and with what result? etc. Who cares?. Certainly not I. No, all I want to do at the present moment is to write good old-fashioned rubbish, or if I am feeling up to it new fashioned rubbish. The fact is when all is boiled down in my great cerebral heap, all rubbish is rubbish, be it old or new, fusty or dirty, Victorian or Georgian.

This, I think, is a new field that needs a great deal of exploration. It has been sadly neglected owing to the extreme boredom and fatigue felt by all students. But for me the case would be different because I am such a keen exponent of the topic in question, and actually, as is evident, complete exercises in it every day. The motto is 'to be a good rubbishman you have got to be fit'. So one has to have one's cerebral dustbin fit, clean and prepared for any piece that may be cast its way. I don't intend to let this matter rot. They say let sleeping dogs lie; I say throw them in the dustbin, and let a good rubbishman pick over them. Enough on rubbish – the lid is on.

Having disposed of that topic I really am stumped for further matter for digression. I am sure no one, not even I, cares for what I did this morning, which was go to Challock and get some apples.

Heigh ho! Someone has arrived – inspiration when I most needed it. M. is tending the problem. I heard the word 'sell' mentioned.

Very interesting, I wait further developments. I don't know if you will get the results; may be you will never know who it was that came on a sunny October day, and what he wanted. I am now going to leave you suspended while I make further enquiries. Suspense is over. It was a man from the village to buy two of Helena's rabbits which is a great relief to everybody. I don't know what she will think about it, but one has gone and the other, I hope, will go tonight. The purchaser was a very nice man, and I think Helena will be well pleased with the home.

Now is the time for few literobatics. I must admit, having said that, I don't much feel like writing along those lines of nonsense. I feel more taken up inside, how can I be light and soft just after I have said my prayers? It is not possible tonight. The effect of my prayers and reading about the Crucifixion takes away mirth, and doesn't leave altogether sadness. It leaves a feeling of fullness and thoughtfulness. The only thing special about my prayers tonight was that I seemed to have a much closer contact, and therefore the reading of the Crucifixion had more reality to it than is usual. For some reason I seem to have tonight a much greater awareness of Christ than is usual;

119

my whole being, as I do anything, seems to be just thinking on him; he is everywhere, he is everything. I prayed for a greater awareness, an opening up of my inside to his presence. He has answered my prayer — what more could I want? It is all very well having awareness, but now by his power He has to mould me and polish me, so that my realisation of his love for me, his concern over my spirit can be transmitted to others. So that his worry and concern for them can be shown. He loves all, and it is our job in life to let him use us to show his love. He made everything, every creation is his, we are nothing. What greater honour than to serve him? But to do that I have got to go a very long way. The words are easy, they are not empty, but the action is difficult; there is pain and suffering in plenty along the way, I know it, everyone knows it, that is why so many stumble and fall.

As I write words like these I often wonder if they are not just the rehash of a programmed mind, but that is not so. Words like that, however many times they may have been read or heard, cannot just be turned out at random. It is not possible, however hard one tries. I have on some occasions, much to my own disgust, tried to make some of my writings more spiritual in their context, because this was originally meant to be a spiritual journal, but try as I might the words never got out of my pen. So you can feel happy, whoever you are, these are my honest thoughts, however strange and misguided they may be; accept them or not as you will. I put no store by them, so don't you either.

I don't want to read and I don't want to go to sleep, so I am left with the only alternative, to waste a bit more paper. It really is slightly farcical — if I carry on at my present rate of production, this Journal will cost me over five pounds. Perhaps (readers) would like to pass round the hat for a little bit of what is good for the pocket, my pocket that is, if my calculations are not too far out.

So ends the anniversary of my birth. Rather like a piece

of wet cabbage hung out of a back window in Soho, but the gaiety is yet to come. Roll on Saturday!

Friday, October 8th
Today has already been very active. It started at eight o'clock because I had to go and have a blood test done, and then we took it straight to Canterbury, so it hasn't been a bad day at all as far as I am concerned, and now I am just off to Ashford.

Here we are again for our little afternoon contribution, so I hope you are all sitting comfortably, and are all eagerly awaiting some piece of subtle literary art which you have come to expect now, owing to the high standards always achieved. You see I am modesty itself! I will have to search through the passages of my grey matter and see what I can turn up in those dusty recesses. The searching is useless — all I can find is a fairly well-tended and tidy corner called 'Excuses for Emptiness'. In fact, it is the best tended, most well-kept little nook that I possess, and I am very proud of it. It is, may be, bordering a little on the bare, over-tended side at the moment, but that is only because I have been constantly round there picking the fruits of its little garden. Oh yes, it has a garden too, where bunches of waffle grow with gay abandon and sprigs of sweetly-scented nonsense may be found poking their fluffly little heads from under stones in the rockery, where the more precocious twaddle rambles in thorny alert. What fun I have tending this little nest day in and day out. In this merry little corner I spend many a happy hour. Time I left it now or it will be even barer than before.

Now we move on to a very grim, grey place almost slum-like in its drabness. This little place is called 'Events'. It is rather Aberdonian in its greyness and I enter today and find that all I have to tell you is that I have managed to get the necessary ingredients to make some Dubonnet and some Cointreau. All rather good fun. I can't imagine what the results will be like.

I am only writing now to put off the fun of starting my brewing, sort of trying to anticipate the fun which I hope it is going to be, but I must go now because I have got to cook up some sugar syrup and I think it must be cold before you add it.

Still not night time, but I have been left on my own for a little longer. The liqueur making was quite a success; not quite as good as I had hoped, but not too bad. The Cointreau I thought was much better than the Dubonnet, but M. doesn't agree. It will be interesting to see what P. thinks. Unfortunately the whole thing was a bit expensive, and didn't take half as long as I had originally hoped.

My vigil is at an end. Antoine is back earlier than usual from work. M. H. and F. are back too, and here is P. It is all happening at once. It is fantastic how that happens; first nobody, then everybody in the space of about two minutes. It is all fun and I am glad that they are all home. Life gets very dull when one is alone, even if you have, like me, a book to recourse to. Now I will stop because I hope that it is about time that they all came in and had tea. I am absolutely famished, even though I had an enormous lunch and have done very little today. Time to go. The book has completed its function and I am well satisfied with it.

Saturday, October 9th

Today is the day of great celebrations. I had to open all my parcels at breakfast. There really were a terrific lot of them, and all the presents were simply marvellous, but I couldn't share my pleasure with everybody else, even though I wanted to. I found it embarrassing for some reason, when one should have found it pleasant and stimulating that everyone wanted to show their feelings towards me by giving.

I have an awful feeling at the moment that I very much want to get out and about and be seeing people, and doing things, but I presume that isn't possible really as I have only been up for about five days – sickening thought that I am always so confined, but fretting about it won't do any good or get anything done as I have said so many times before.

I had a very sad piece of news this morning, that Aunt Hope has had a brain operation, and the awful thing is that I never knew, and consequently I didn't do anything about it. I didn't pray or write, I should have done both, but instead I carried on as normal writing to Uncle Bill about business, not knowing the strain he must have been under the whole time. It is terrible, but there it is.

I think at present that I might go to Ashford and take my clock in to be mended. I got a new one for my birthday and it seems to be overwound – such is life. Now I will see what I can write. Antoine thoroughly overdid my birthday by getting me some cigars, tobacco and two plastic buckets for home brewing; so nice of him. Last night I found it a little difficult to go to sleep, so I tried the book that M. liked by Elizabeth Goudge – it really is very good indeed. Writing at the moment is proving very difficult. I lie here looking for inspiration, my head laid back, staring at the ceiling. All I can see is a spider. Inspiration has come. I must go to Lenham to pick up some pills and a prescription – what a bore, but never mind, I must have them.

Sunday, October 10th
This morning my leg is rather uncomfortable, but not badly so. Being Sunday the Vicar is coming here to give communion.

I never really understand what it is that communion does for me, but it does something very joyous and important. That joy I think is the love of God, or certainly the knowledge of it overflowing out of one. It is an infectious joy or love because one can feel greater love for others so much more easily after communion. Unless one is very holy I think communion, taken too frequently, could lead to a loss of its value, but to someone truly holy it is a vital part of every day. My trouble is that I haven't realised its full meaning and importance. I always pray that I may understand it more fully; my prayers I know will be answered, but how, one never knows for sure. Sometimes one doesn't know that one's prayers have been answered until a little time after, and then if you are like me, you likely as not forget to thank Christ for his answering. The sorrow I must cause Christ with my failure, my weakness and sin is awful to me. It is like saying to one's greatest friend ... I am sorry I can't find words to describe the awfulness of my failures and the pain they cause Christ. I hope I do sometimes, otherwise my life isn't worth living. Here is the Vicar for Communion – help me Lord to understand.

A truly lovely service. It brings Christ right to the house; the Presence is so much there. A service in the home is wonderful, it has something that a church service can lack; but the reverse is also true.

I did something rather selfish this morning. Angela came in to keep me company because she wasn't going to be here long, and I wrote my book. I have all the rest of the day to write it, but I had to do it then; how stupid could I be? I should take every opportunity of her company I can, and now she is gone for another four weeks.

It is very strange, but when I am in bed, as at present, I always have something to do, as though being in bed was an occupation in itself. Lying in bed and doing nothing is all right, while being up and doing nothing is appallingly boring.

I want very much to carry on writing, so I am sorry to say that you will just have to be patient with me a little longer. It is odd this way that I write to an audience, and yet I am sure that no-one except me will read it, (or be capable of deciphering it), but as this writing is for God I have to rely on some audience. I say to myself that this is dedicated to God but it is a very difficult thing to accomplish, and the only way I can achieve it is by writing as I always do. This leads me to the impression that I am writing, not for God, but for man. Is it possible that, by writing for God, I am also writing for man and vice versa? Time, the old leveller, will tell.

I have said my prayers and read my Bible. I found the latter almost impossible as I was so incredibly tired. I am now just trying to write as an experiment, to find whether it is easier to read or write. I will have to wait for a bit for the stimulation of change to wear off. When I was reading the Old Testament I had to keep on shaking my head at intervals to clear the sight. I am just beginning to think it is easier to write; must be the activity of moving the hand. No, I am beginning to go. I just have to shut my eyes and I am dreaming in about one minute. It is a lovely position to be in, to know that all one has to do is close one's eyes and one is asleep. I think I will go now – no point in hanging around here, even though I would quite like to carry on for a bit.

The time is a quarter to three in the morning. My leg is trembling and hurting and I seem to feel weak all over – I can't imagine what is wrong. I have never felt like this before, it feels like something different. It can't be too bad, otherwise I wouldn't be writing so happily. Since I went to sleep I have been living in a sort of waking-sleeping dream. One will be just under and just about dreaming, when all of a sudden one will be wide awake and listening acutely to something, trembling slightly and wondering what it was that woke one. My trembling has turned to a feeling of sickness. What a night. I don't really mind, and I am not really worried about myself or anything else at present. It is very strange how gay and amusing one is at this time of night.

M. woke and we had a jolly amusing time — maybe it is that one's mentality is lower and therefore everything appears that much more amusing. I am beginning to feel really rather tired; the lines are doing their slow and stately dance, and the words are following them very happily. I really must see if I can do something about them, like trying to relax, but it is so much easier said than done. I have an awfully long way to go to finish this page off, and it is going, I know, to take about ten times as long.

Monday, October 11th
I have only this moment just woken up, but here I am, as faithful as ever, feeling tired, sick and uncomfortable, but somehow these things are irrelevant and unimportant. I don't think that I will be writing very much as I just had some peths; these make life very hazy and difficult to control, so don't expect too much from the pen this morning.

I have been asleep now since half past eight and the time at present is eleven o'clock, so I made up for missed minutes. Writing at present is a trifle difficult as M. has set up an ironing shop in the drawing room. It is very difficult to concentrate, but I wouldn't have her move for anything; her company is very good. I am beginning to feel the effects of the peths I have just been given . . .

Writing is easier at present because M. is concentrating on her ironing rather than concentrating on me.

Last night I itched all over, everything tickled, as though I were in a bed of thistle-down. My legs, back, chest, they all itched; there was no area of demarcation, even my head itched for a little while. Last night was a pretty strange night altogether. I have a feeling, sorry to harp about my health, that I have become immune to peths; they never seem to cure pain these days. Injections are the only sure method of relief, and I am not too keen on them, as may be imagined. This morning's contribution has been on the whole pretty brown and heavy.

I just suddenly felt like adding a little bit of murk to my dark brown soup. Partly because I want to go to sleep and partly because I am nearing the end of this book, and the thought of starting a new one is really quite exciting. M. is still busily ironing and every now and again I feel as though I am being scrutinised very carefully, but when I look up she is fully concentrated on her work.

My prayers this evening were very difficult owing to the influence of drugs and pills. My mind was simply impossible to control. I was dreaming while I was actually awake. The whole object was very difficult but I know that He understands the problem, but that doesn't mean that I don't pray because it is too difficult. On the contrary, I try that much harder, or rather let him try that much harder for me. It is Christ that is in me that prays if I would only let him. If my prayers are difficult, I think it may mean that I am not rested enough into Christ or I am travelling through a dry period. Both are pretty much the same, but it is at times like these that one's faith is refined. I must never give up trying. If spontaneous mental prayer becomes too difficult because of fatigue or drugs or anything else, then I must resort to pattern prayers, either read out of a book or from memory. But these must only be used in special circumstances − I don't think there is anything to replace spontaneous prayer. This is straining for the living waters, for refreshment and encouragement. Everything necessary can be gleaned from the Lord's Prayer, but the very special private needs of the christian soul at a particular time can only be, I think, effectively dealt with by spontaneous prayer.

Just by the by, something else I do as an alternative to spontaneous prayer is to say the Lord's Prayer very slowly, thinking over each phrase as it comes up, and turning them into the main topic for spontaneous prayer. People go through the Lord's Prayer much too fast, not realising at all its vast, almost limitless meanings. I am sorry to thrust my little theories and practices at you, I don't know why I did, because I didn't actually enjoy doing it, and it may seem that I am saying 'This is the way to do it.' If anyone does read these words, do remember that they are just my thoughts, ideas and practices, and in no way am I trying to instruct at all. I would not dare.

Now having got myself thoroughly tangled up, I think I will call it a day. This faint ink certainly puts pressure on the old peepers. I can hardly see what I have written and the constant peering for the ghostly letters strains the eyeballs and makes eyelids heavy and apparently long over due for hanging down.

Tuesday, October 12th

I woke up this morning in extreme discomfort – that was at about five o'clock, and tried to summon M. on the blower, but it seemed to have packed up altogether, so I had to finish up by shouting, which got her eventually. The time now is quarter past six, and the only reason I am writing is that I have had an injection and some peths, so things ought to take a pretty hazy turn quite soon. The ink, which was so faint last night, seems to have coloured up a little and I would go as far as to say it looks absolutely normal. I did think that it was acting a trifle strange, when it felt so dry to write with; it was really quite an effort. It doesn't take very long for the pills to get blurring, let's just hope I can make the bottom of the page in one piece. I think I should be able to, I have only two lines to go – one can write anything on two lines.

The time is twenty-five to seven and I can hear P. getting up to feed the pigs, poor chap, it is a beautiful deep

128

twilight blue outside, with the blackbirds making continuous alarm calls and the bantams crowing on and off. This time of morning, this feeling of the air and the noise of the birds, all remind me of the days when I used to feed in the morning. How I miss it. I am sure that if I actually were feeding the cattle now I wouldn't be so nostalgic about it, but I can't help it. I think I will have to stop now for a snooze, to clear the vision and stimulate the brain, which has gone rather like a bowl of hot spinach. The time is seven o'clock and I feel worse than I did before Swanley woke me up. I have little or no control over my muscles at all, my hands are shaking and my head's humming; even my pen seems pretty incapable of writing thoughtfully and constructively. If I could stay a little longer you might get daytime dreams, which are always interesting, but sadly I must go to sleep.

Monday, October 11th

Before I do anything else with this new book I am going to give this pen a good wash out, because it is making it far too difficult to write, so you will just have to wait a little while. There, I think is quite a satisfactory difference. Instead of scraping loathingly over the pages, it is flowing gently and smoothly. The trouble wasn't fungal growth in the flow channel as I feared, but something worse, curdled ink. This is a more dangerous disease as it can lead to the blocking of funnels, channels and vents, and also a piece of ink-curd can be a nucleus for curd growth, which inevitably leads to tubular thrombosis. I wouldn't have given my pen much longer if I hadn't operated when I did.

I have been asleep for what feels like hours, and I woke up refreshed and full of go. I look at my watch and find that I have in fact been asleep for seven minutes. Immediately the lines begin to bend, the words I have just written start to disappear, and run gaily into each other. At least writing is more feasible than reading, the latter being very nearly impossible. Actually neither are much fun. I have been a very good boy – I have written all my 'thank you' letters which is a great relief. It is the sort of job I can put off, and put off until it becomes impossible to write at all, and my conscience gets to the stage where it says that it would be ruder to write than not to write at all.

The time is ten past five and I have just woken up after a sleep of something like two and a half hours, but the sleep as yet doesn't seem to have made much difference to my eyesight, which is still very much all over the shop. If my eyes don't start behaving themselves I am going to give them a cold bath – they have no reason for behaving like this. I am afraid I will have to carry out my threat. It will be an interesting experiment at least. There, I have completed the experiment on my eyes and I can't honestly say whether it is a success or failure. It is a messy mixture of both; I am not brilliantly bright eyed and awake, and on the other hand I am not completely dopey. Hold on, it seems to me that I am rapidly going that way, dopey I mean. It seems that the effect of the cold flannel was rather short-lived, and now I am back where I started.

My prayers will be very tricky tonight I fear, but I have got hold of, or to be more honest, M. has, Elizabeth Goudge's anthology of prayer and I will probably read a few, rather than try praying myself. As I said last night, only on special occasions; this is very definitely one of those.

Tuesday October 12th

I am writing as soon as possible, because last night I got very little sleep at all. Hence as soon as I put my pen to paper my sight seems to be going to go. This little sentence in itself seems a fairly good advertisement for the sort of thing to be expected. As well as me being awake, M., I think, spent a lot of the time awake with me, but she, as all mothers, is used to it and seems to be fairly resilient when it comes to all night vigils.

I do hope the doctor will have something for my leg, as at times last night it was excruciatingly painful. Excruciating sounds like something to do with knees, but that is irrelevant. What is plain is that I think only half of my brain is functioning properly, the other half being asleep or being much that way inclined, and as I have such a small brain capacity, when half of it is taking a well deserved rest, not much can be expected.

I think I have just been asleep for the last few minutes — half an hour to be precise — but it has had noticeable results. As M. says, I must sleep by day and rest by night! Helena has been in and out to say good-bye before she goes to school, which is an unaccustomed honour.

I think I will catch up on my sleep now as things are beginning to bend about a bit. I think I am in full control of my faculties, I have slept pretty solidly from when I woke up for my breakfast to half past one. That should be enough one would have thought, but apparently it is not. I am trembling and bending all over the shop. Even though it is only half one, I reckon that I will finish my day's scribbling when I have reached the bottom of the page. After that I think I will attempt to read a bit. My eyeballs aren't shaking while my hands and fingers are, so one would have thought the former would be the easier. I have just tried to do some reading — I should be all right for a few more minutes. But having said that I have nothing to say except my right shoulder is sore. I must stop now otherwise I will disintegrate into a uselesss heap.

I have been asleep and woke up at 5.30 in the evening not knowing where on earth I was. Most of today has been a kind of daylight dream. Please, please, bear with me.

The wind is howling outside and everything is very dark, black and wet; there are no shapes to speak of. This caused me some considerable thought. Why so dark at eight o'clock? The answer was that it was night time. M. and Helena have gone to get my pills; I really do need them. Every time I woke up I thought the day was over. It

131

has finished quite a few times, but I still have the tedious old night to encounter which will be a terrible ordeal because I have been asleep most of the time. I am declaring, now that my leg is much much better, it doesn't hurt. Now all I have to decide is, which arm it is, I think it is the right one, that is fairly uncomfortable. I must leave off and go back to sleep.

Wednesday, October l3th
The only reason these words are being written is for the sake of completion, so if I don't write them a date will be missed.

Friday, October 15th
Today I am going to write nothing as all these pills and injections have made me lose any sense of reason that I ever had. 'Do just bear with me for a few days.'

Sunday, 17th October
This may be the last of these awfully messy days. Let's hope I can do it without foul splodging or crossing out, or mess which has been usual for the last page or two.

Apparently John and Sally were praying for me to be cured quickly with their prayer group. What better proof that the power of the Spirit is still strong. Last night I went to sleep in pain; this morning I woke up in comfort. It has happened before, but I haven't known it. I will thank them.

My writing is a little slow and plodding but I can promise you, little words, that it is all true – I am better. There is nothing to stop me being up very shortly indeed. Do you know that I have just looked back over the last week's scrawlings and realised that still I am not myself. I had written the wrong date down, so the general mess continues. Now I have checked all up, my watch, my Almanack and they all say October 17th, which is a great relief because sometimes they threatened to put me into

November or back to 16th October; but I am glad to say, here I am. My eyes have just started to do that famous little calypso of theirs — the one that makes everything go up and down as if they owned it.

I have fully recovered as far as I can tell (well as fully as I will today anyway). I am lying in the absolute luxury of a bed that P. has made for me. I went into communion worried, and concerned that the pills were going to make me dopey and completely unresponsive. As usual I needn't have worried; the effect of communion was joy, health, light and peace. It is all things that are good. My communion was very much like the weather that we had during it. It started off with pouring, blinding rain and finished with purifying brilliant sun. The sort of sun that is seen through waterfalls, or seen through chestnut or beech-wood, filtered light. The illusion soon passes like the weather, but he sends us his ever brightening visions of himself in the strangest of places and the ability to discover his strength. I often wonder to myself whether it is not easier to discover true faith in some country where the faith is not allowed, than in a free country like England or America, where it is allowed and professed.

A blue-bottle has decided to turn my life into misery; it doesn't take them very long to do that. It has made life so frustrating that I may have to call through for some fly-spray. The mere mention of that deathly word and there was catacombal silence, but I will still send for some. The whole incident is over — not a drop of blood was shed by any side. Mummy came through armed with spray and tea towel. Then she had a brain wave — 'Open the window.' She did, the blue-bottle flew out happy and unharmed.

Mummy has just told me two of the things I said when I was ill and feverish. One was 'Who is a greedy boy then', and 'Just off to have a natter with the clothes moths'!

Pa is up to his eyes in electrical speak-boxes, because Legs, that dear dog that we were asked to look after for a week, got tangled up in the wires and pulled it off the top of the dresser. Pa, unlike him, I think has declared it past repair, but he is giving it one last try; very frustrating and fiddly work for a man with big fingers. You won't believe it, but Pa's trouser legs now seen from a certain angle, and in a certain light, look like an advertisement for Jo Grimond; looking at them straight I don't see how that could be possible, but I honestly promise you it is true. Pa, after two and a half hours' struggle, has, I think, finally given up.

I just wanted to say what a great, great man St Paul was. As well as being stoned, chased from town to town, he was flogged, beaten chained to walls overnight and on top of this he had this curious infliction which he prayed could be removed from him. He had everything to fight against. Words are not enough to describe him, but I just felt I wanted to tell someone how I admire and respect him.

Turdus, James's blackbird, has yet again taken a flight for it. It is twenty past six – the latest flight out he has ever made. Maybe the allurements of the friend in the hedge down by the stream, are greater than those we can offer. One beautiful thing that we can say about Turdus: we wanted to keep him but when he wanted to go, he could. If only he could have stayed long enough for James to see him. I think I may be a bit pessimistic, he might come back, but this is so horribly like the good old repetitive way of fate, foul beast.

Everybody just beginning to feel happy, then 'pouf', all is gall and wormwood, but the thing to remember is that through the love of God, gall and wormwood can be made beautiful, and it is only one's own bleary eyes that restrict the obvious vision. M. and P. are busily arguing about who should go and have the bath first, thus both wasting precious time – such is life!

I closed my eyes and let my imagination go. I was at the end of a big long room, rough hewn walls, lighted. I was chained to this chair, and thus to the room, which was my prison. Every link was a link of an individual chain, every link in the same chain had the same feel, they either irritated, drew blood, were cold or hot, these were the only ones I could feel. What were the unfeelable ones doing to me? They must be eating out my very spirit. 'Oh Jesus', I said; there was a momentary relief. I tried again, 'Oh Jesus, Son of God'. The pain left my body. I had the answer now, the chains were dropping like scales. 'Oh Jesus Christ, Son of God, forgive me, sinner that I am.' Light poured in, the room throbbed with light, Jesus Christ, Son of God stepped forward, embraced me, and guided me out. I was free.

Why I wrote that I don't know at all, but I felt that I had to. When I had finished I put my pen down and heaved a sigh of relief and thought what a lot I had written, but looking back, it is pathetic and flimsy. Maybe a good sleep after all those pills would not be a bad idea.

The knight was still bound in that chair, he could move all his ligaments, he could shout, but he couldn't leave his seat. He began to sweat with effort; he took off his helmet and chain-mail, he was left standing, a widening gulf between Jesus and him, what must he leave – what could he do? He threw his sword into the water and leapt over the gulf. There were tears in the eyes of Jesus, the effort had been very great. The prodigal son had returned.

I think that I will have to spend the whole of today gently writing and snoozing because even with reading and writing I am extremely hard pressed. The terrible thing is that it is such an effort.

I have had a big wash and brush up and feel so clean, so

fresh and clean, that I want to tell you all about it. I feel like a bowling fresh wind coming down the mountainside; not one of those red in the face fat sweaty jobs encountered from time to time on old maps but the sort that bends the poplars, blows leaves about and is loved by children for the piles of soft debris it collects for them to shuffle in.

I think as it is twenty past one I will go to sleep until lunch and then I will wake up all fresh for my nice new young nurse who is coming to look after me. I will try and tell you all. This super-powered white work nurse doesn't arrive here for another ten minutes. The longer the time she has over her allotted arrival date the higher will be my estimation of her. It is all very interesting. Every change in the note of the wind is a car to me; I wish she would get her arrival over. I feel very let down by the people; they said she would arrive at two o'clock and now it is three.

As I said, it is three o'clock, the nurse never arrived, and so Mrs. Langford is going to act as a stand in for an hour. Much simpler. The head of the Nursing Agency said it was very strange, and very unlike capable twenty-eight-year-old Miss So and So, and could only put it down to mechanical failure. I pray for her that it is nothing worse, like an accident.

I wonder if I mentioned to you how unruly are my old pins, they really will only stagger a few steps and then they are sore, worn-out and useless. Something must be done about the pins, I reckon; maybe a physio course wouldn't do them any harm. I want them to get strong and useful again.

Now I am going to sleep, snooze or read and await events. Everything got much more painful this afternoon, I got M. to give me an injection and half an hour later some pills, which sent me beautifully and fast to sleep, until everybody came home; then I really did feel bad, so Pa came and read to me until I went to sleep.

But today has been a beautiful day, everything about it

has been perfect and right, and looking back on it I feel that it has been a day truly well spent. I say this only because it gives me a feeling of satisfaction and fulfilment, which I cannot describe.

Tuesday, October 19th

The most important thing to remember every morning as I set out to write this Journal is that it is dedicated and written for God; every word is written for him to do with what he likes. By so remembering I should be able to start off with some interesting thought. I have set up a bargain; I think it only right that my book and its words be used by God, but that I can write anything I like.

This morning I picked up my pen, full of joy and for some reason gratitude. Was it joy that the weather was so wild and free, or was it gratitude to God for giving me the ability to write. 'To be able to write', few people seem to realise, is a very very great talent; your talent like mine may be a bit rusty and not shine as much as some of your others. But if you lost it how you would search the house for it, how you would pray for it and weep for it! If you have a talent, even though he be a trifle rusty and dirty, polish him up and develop him. Practice is the best method of polishing; with a lot of use all talents shine. It is one's job in life to do everything to the best of one's ability and for the glory of God, because nothing comes from us to others except through God.

That marvellous feeling of sleepiness is beginning to overtake me for a change. Just as I think to myself 'Heigh ho', here we are on to a winner, down come the shutters. It really limits the amount one can write!

We are awake once more and M. was very sympathetic. Nice as this is, one must always treat sympathy with respect, otherwise one soon becomes very, very sorry for oneself. Sympathy is like the driest fuel to the fire of self pity; sympathy is always good, but be careful where it goes. Make sure it will do more good than harm.

Yesterday P. did something very special and important. You will never be able to guess what it was, so I won't hold you in suspense, I won't keep you dangling on the hooks of desire. I am not that mean, or brought up to torture; I don't get pleasure, or rather never did get pleasure from tearing up petals or butterflies, so you can see that I am really a very nice chap and wouldn't in any circumstances stretch you out thirsting in the desert for knowledge. I am sure you are dying to know – he got me two more of these note-books, so now I really am swamped with them. It has given me an almost hopeless feeling!

I just dreamt that I was in an entirely white room with arched ceilings and pillars dividing into three parts the room, the whole room led up to an enormous organ pedestal and on that pedestal an organ was turning round to face us. It was beautiful. Everything about the organ was perfect, it's symmetry and facade were unspeakable. Then a curious thing happened, it split in half and opened up, showing to me its entrails, its tubes, old pipes, torn bits of cloth – it was sordid compared with what I had just seen, something worthy of the dustbin men. It closed again and once more was perfect, not a blemish, not a scratch, but just showing me that all that is perfect on the outside may not be so good on the inside, and also showing me that a superlative noise can come from what looks like a pile of old junk. That dream took about five seconds, and don't forget it didn't have any pretty little contrite interpretations added by me. It was just the whole thing in its five second surrealism.

Think how I must have felt in a silent white marble and plaster hall, with a white organ turning silently and opening on me. Anyway enough; if I haven't got the effect over, I don't deserve to succeed, and anything I add now isn't going to help you, or me. The general effect I think is a bit tatty and second-rate and means nothing at all or very little anyway. I am not going to leave that as a statement, because extraordinary things can help other people. Something you would imagine would normally nauseate someone, in fact turns out to be their retrieving hand. This is the only thing for them at the time, so as I am writing this for God, anything said could be of potential use to someone. Therefore, I must not say that all I have said is a waste of time, because it is not.

I will finish up this page by saying that I think I am suffering from the worst sore throat I have ever had. It makes all the others look like midge bites beside a hornet's stings; that's how bad it is; that still doesn't really describe it; I reckon it is very very bad indeed, and I am very sorry for myself. I have just forced M. to look into my mouth; what joy she gave me, she didn't let me down as far as sympathetic expletives were required, she had them all. And now I really can feel sorry for myself.

P. has just come home and given me lots of sympathy; if I am not careful I will find this hurting more than it usually does; such is the effect of sympathy.

Wednesday, October 20th
Yesterday was really highly chaotic by the end, that is after I had finished writing, because my sore throat got worse and worse to such an* extent that I could hardly breathe. Highly alarming it was, I can tell you. Anyway the doctor came and sorted one or two things out and I spent a fairly comfortable night. M. got three hours sleep altogether . . .

I owe, I think, everyone an apology. All today's writings have been about me; it shows how important I think myself.

Last night, during some of the worst moments, M. read to me my, and I know her, favourite piece of the Bible. They are chapters 14, 15 and 16 of the Gospel of St John.

* He very nearly died from this 'sore throat'. As he says, he could hardly breathe.

Last night I found them so soothing and relaxing, so peaceful, yet so passionate and moving, and yet they were the words of a man deeply concerned for the spiritual well-being and the physical well-being of his friends when he wasn't going to be able to do anything for them, except try and prepare them. St John was a very dear sweet man, he was Jesus' special friend on earth. One can feel John's personality come out all through his Gospel, but most especially during the farewell discourses. During these, and these only, do you realise the full extent of Jesus' love for His disciples, and I think John, with his extra perceptive friend's concern, is the only disciple to realise fully what is going on. He was the only disciple to keep his head during the ensuing conflict. The reason for this was he knew it was going to happen all along.

How did I get on to the subject? Yes, we read the discourses last night. They were only possible because John knew Jesus as a true friend, not as a Rabbi but as a dear, dear friend, and the discourses were possible because John could feel Jesus' concern for him as a friend. I think I may have said all this before. If I have, I am sorry to have bored you.

I would just like to say how comfortable and happy I am, lying here on a bed of cushions in the mellow warm light of my bedside lamp, with the sure company of P. next door at my beck and call, ready to help me in any way that I could possibly need. When I say beck and call, I don't mean that he is out there waiting specially for me; he happens to be in the only place where he can do his school work without being disturbed. It doesn't seem to me as though he cares whether he is disturbed or not; he has just turned on the loudest and most revolting music.

I am very sleepy, but I thought I would just say what happened in my prayers. I started off trying to say them on my own, and all I managed to get was a picture of a round table of huge prawn shrimplike creatures, waving their claws and creepers in the air. I was then disturbed, thankfully, from this nightmare and I managed to get M. to get me Father Andrew's book of Prayers, where I just managed a prayer of Adoration, a Personal Prayer, and a Prayer of Thanksgiving. Having read those, the effort was greater than would be expected, I tried about five times to say the Lord's Prayer. Every time except one, I think (I emphasise the 'I think') I went into some sort of inane sleep. This occurrence, coupled with the beauty of Father Andrews' Prayers, shows the necessity for the printed prayer, and how I can't rely entirely on spontaneous prayer.

Thursday, October 21st

The nurse that didn't turn up on Monday, bless her, is turning up this afternoon, or rather a substitute for the miscreant is turning up. I don't want nurses hanging around. It's bad enough being in bed, but to have strange nurses hanging around is off, I reckon. That is only a purely selfish attitude, because unless every now and again we have one of these people, it means M. can never get out, as I spend most of my time in or between beds. My idea of no nurses is not really on.

This morning after I had woken, I tried to stand up. It really was disappointingly hard work. It feels as if I am going to have to learn that very difficult art form all over again. It was just the terrific weight that struck me as being strange and also the buckling feeling from behind the knees, which I haven't noticed before.

I have discovered why I am gloomy – the cause is heat. I am laid out under blankets with the sun's heat blazing through the panes of glass magnified a few times over, just having to sweat it out. That is hard work too. With this excuse I feel I have a reason to feel a little down in the mouth.

This morning, a present M. ordered for my birthday

arrived. It was a book by Thomas Merton called *No Man is an Island*. I don't know what it is going to be like; the author said it was a precedent to *Seeds of Contemplation* and was simpler. So it should be just up my street; I found *Seeds of Contemplation* in parts too advanced and difficult. No two people develop at the same rate. Something that to someone is very easy to understand, to someone else is double dutch. So by reading both books, I should get the benefit of both worlds. All very philosophical and I am sure none of it is true. All the same I am very pleased to get the book, because it is a lovely edition to get and also a difficult book to get hold of – all my books are, apparently – I can't understand why. It seems foolish to me that they don't print more, because there is a terrific market proved by the demand.

The Sign of Jonas was very difficult to get. In fact in the end we got it secondhand at some junk dealers. The same with *Seeds of Contemplation*. All the other Merton books have come from the Library. Even though it was got for me, I don't intend to keep it as my own, because already I can feel little possessive urges building up, saying how nice it is all yours. It can go in your own little library. This isn't to be the case, I don't want to possess it, I want everyone to possess it. It can go in the communal library anywhere in the house. I am glad that I have got that off my chest. It may seem childish but it really has been worrying me quite a bit.

This phantom nurse is to arrive in twenty-five minutes. I don't think I have ever been quite so upset about anything so petty before in my whole life, but the fact is that I am in such a terribly 'one down position' (using S. Potter's terminology). I am alone, half naked, in bed, and not ready for any physical combat. Also the brain is working below normal output; by that I mean my usually speedy repartees are slightly blunted. So as you can well see, I am in a fix. To start with, to get her one-upness in good working order, I should think that she will be bright, breezy, self-confident and above all crisp and white. This immediately makes the patient feel hot, fed up, tired, angry and above all dirty. That is only the beginning. What comes on from that point is quite unfair blow by blow destruction of the patient.

She has arrived. I don't really know what to make of her. She seems a kindly enough old soul, about forty-five I should say; maybe getting on fifty-three. She has introduced herself, made herself useful and has decided to push off and do some reading. Where, I don't know. I fear she is in the next-door room which I will find a little trying as her presence and spirit will be here, but not her form. Ah well, let's hope for the best.

I have just plucked up the courage to ask the lady from next door to come through and open the window. What fun over one window. I didn't think it would be possible, but eventually she managed it. Originally she opened it not far enough, and then too far so she had to get on a stool to correct it again. There I am being unduly critical – her job is much more difficult than mine. I should be very grateful to her that she is taking the strain off M. so that she can get a decent rest this afternoon, and yet not feel worried about me in the least, knowing that I have been left in good capable trained hands. Apparently I have, according to all the initials and badges dotted over her chest, some of them most impressive.

There, I went to sleep, so I didn't have to feel that I had to entertain the nurse next door. I do hope P. hurries up because he is taking her to the station. My estimation of her must have gone up 99 per cent because for her holidays she helps take four hundred physically and mentally handicapped children to Lourdes. Also her parents are disabled; she lives with them and spends her other time working for old people. Her whole life devoted to other people. May the last come first, and the first come last. That applies so much to her. She is the sort of person that one very rarely meets or when one does, doesn't know anything about, because they are shy and retiring, and here am I all too keen to get her out of the house, because I find her difficult to talk to. You must know how I feel now; I am thoroughly ashamed of myself.

There, the nurse has gone. She went quickly out, hardly waiting for a word of thanks, poor little dear, never to be seen again I should think, by me.

Friday, October 22nd

This morning I saw something which I haven't seen for a long time; it gave me the most unpleasant shock — it was my partly-bearded face. What a sight for sore eyes! When I had shaved it, it was even worse. I don't know if that was just my usual vanity, or if it was disappointment at having to shave off what seemed to me such a manly growth, but to tell you the truth, my manly growth wouldn't make many an old lady's moustache blush. It was just about getting along that way, more to be ashamed of than proud of, but now it is done and I am quite well pleased.

I was just thinking about yesterday and retrospectively I hated every part of it I think. The morning because I spent it asleep, the afternoon because I had that nurse; the only part I did enjoy was after the nurse had left because, as I forgot to tell you, Vi came to see me which was very sweet of her. She brought with her a marvellous smelling bouquet of flowers, made up of lavender, verbena, honeysuckle and roses.

M. is now going to come and keep me company with her ironing. I have just told her what I thought about the nurse yesterday, which wasn't much from the nurse's point of view, and I think a bit of a blow as far as M. was concerned.

She has just brought Turdus in here; he has changed quite a lot since I last saw him. The first thing he did was to take a grape from my hand and fly off and eat it.

The last pleasant thing that I wanted to tell you about

144

was the fact that P. read me the first few paragraphs of the first chapter of Thomas Merton. It makes it so much better being read, because one doesn't have to make sense of the punctuation, and therefore can follow more closely the meaning of the words. In this particudlar case the words had to be followed very carefully. I still haven't got the full meaning of them, though I have read it through to myself alone twice since. He has tackled an extremely difficult problem and has put every inflection into it that he could. How he manages to see so deeply into a problem strikes me as extraordinary. He finds paradoxes and subjects for discussion where I would never dream of looking or going. I presume my simplicity is my luck. If I found all these problems now, while I was still trying to find my faith, I would be in a terrible state.

Saturday, October 23rd

From my position in bed, unless I make a terrific effort, I can't see the view out of my window; all I can see is the sky. Nothing struck me as out of the ordinary this morning until I saw a bird fly across my horizon. It was blurred. The fog was like soup. Since I have been in bed I have stopped noticing the changes in scenery and weather, so when I get up, which I hope ought to be quite soon, I ought to be in for one or two interesting changes, especially as far as the trees are concerned. The noises that are coming in the window are superbly autumnal, being made up mostly of the squeaky and clacky noises of starlings, and the occasional robin.

Antoine has just been in to see me, he really is an extremely nice fellow. I hadn't seen him for about a week, so it was a welcomed visit. He has now been whisked off to hold Helena's hand while she takes her rabbits to the vet, where they are going to have various stitches removed and lumps looked at. They seem to be very lump prone; this is the third attack of lumps that has occurred in the last month.

This afternoon P. and I ventured into the world of model making, much to my eventual discomfort, because it made me so very stiff that by the time we had finished I had to have an injection.

Time has passed rapidly and I have just finished my supper. Meals are always very disappointing in bed, because they take such a terribly short time and you can't have the interesting conversations that one gets with a normal meal. My supper tonight of steak pie and apple took me five minutes at the most; useless as a time waster unless you happen to be reading or watching television.

At the moment I am feeling very sorry for myself, cut off and left out. So I have just hailed everybody in the kitchen on the blower as they seem to have finished supper. It is the lying here in the light of the bedside lamp in such quiet that makes everything so lonely. I will soon have company I hope, but things can take time. If I was a good Christian I would be able to use this time to meditate in.

I have had company now for hours; Liz sat in here talking to me, ever since I started complaining and feeling sorry for myself. Very good company, too. She doesn't force conversation, she just sits and lets yours soak in and then lets something interesting soak back at you without any apparent effort.

I have just had a bad attack of stiff arm, which I thought might limit my daily output, a short rest and a rub soon put it right. It must just have been some muscles twisted around each other's necks.

I have just had one of those unpleasant moments of thought, which occur to me so rarely, but when they do, I don't like them. This little moment was, when am I going to get better, and how is this illness going to affect the rest of my life? It is just the impermanence of it all that worries me. I know it needn't, because Christ is looking after me, but I have such weak faith that it is easily moved by these thoughts. It is incredible how quickly lurid thoughts can manifest themselves if allowed, and the terrible thing is that every now and then I let them, so I can be frightened and sorry for myself. I can honestly say I let them happen, perhaps once every two months, sometimes even less than that. It usually takes something to spark it off. I remember the last time I let things worry me in any way at all was when I was told that I was getting fat in the face, because of the pills I was taking. I knew that anyway, but I just let it worry me. Externally I laughed it off, but inside it really did concern me. It doesn't any more because I am completely used to the idea and, happily to say, the little old face that goes with it. It was the latter that was the difficult part. It used to give me rather a horrible shock when I caught a glimpse of my face in the mirror, but I am quite used to it now.

Monday, October 25th

It is very sad, but the house empties itself today. The weekend is over, James is going to London, P. and Helena back to school; that just leaves M. and me as usual. But I have the mammoth work to do so I have no lack of occupation.

Turdus spent the whole of last night out and arrived back in the kitchen at breakfast. He really has trained himself very well indeed. I have just been looking back to a week and a half ago when I was ill. It is going to be quite a job deciphering the mess.

One very nice thing is that P. has got the day off and at the moment he is sitting in my room reading the newspaper. It is extraordinary what a difference just a presence makes. If I was alone I would be feeling sorry for myself and lonely, but as it is I am not.

It is teatime, everything is silent and I am fed up and lonely. I am sick of being ill.

I am a little better now as I have just had a visit from Antoine, with all his visas, permits and passports. It is very interesting and complicated. He provided me with the necessary interest to perk up a bit. It is very odd I am still feeling very hot and my eyesight isn't very good. I hope all is O.K. on the Western Front. I allow myself to become worried rather easily now-a-days. I never know what is going to happen next. There, all is now better. I have got some attention which is what I needed. The sooner I get up the better, but I don't think today will do. It will have to wait; even then I will have nothing to do. This next convalescence is going to take a lousy old time I fear. Here I am thinking about it, and I haven't yet embarked upon it. I am sorry my mind is just full of morbid thoughts — everything at present is gall and wormwood.

Wednesday, October 27th

Yesterday was truly desperate and I was desperate; let's hope today is better. Last night was pretty hectic. I woke up with a sore throat followed by a nose bleed, the latter has carried slowly on into this morning and is still going, but I am sure no-one, not even me, is interested in my ailments.

My faith, for some reason, has taken a serious knock these last couple of days. I have lost my urge and keenness. Maybe I am just travelling through a dry patch, but if that is the case, it is the driest patch I have ever encountered. It has got to the stage where I can't understand the point of anything. I presume in some ways I should welcome it, this dryness, as it is a chance to show my faith, but with the feelings I have in the pit of my stomach, feelings of anger, fear and frustration, I am more worried, worried that my faith should prove as weak as me. Maybe it would be a good thing to have my pathetic weakness shown to me, so that I can place more faith elsewhere, not entirely in myself which I presume is what I have been doing. All I can do is hope and wait for help. It will come, I know that, if I have the faith to wait long enough. That is the test. I am beginning to feel better already; just by admitting my situation some of the tension has left me.

This morning I actually got up for the first time and staggered drunkenly next door into the drawing room. It is horrific how quickly muscles degenerate. Mine, which have had rather a lot of practice at degeneration and regeneration, seem to find the former about ninety times as easy as the latter. So it means that they have been getting progressively weaker and weaker over the last year. Nothing desperately exciting has happened this morning except I had a bed bath and I have peeled some apples, all sorts of mundane little tasks are to me valuable as a form of occupation. What I desperately need is something to do with my hands.

When I got up this morning I spent some time at the window. The trees have turned in the last few days. I left the leaves green and leathery, and now they are brown and falling. If it hadn't been for the sun shining straight at me, I might have been able to see more. I could only see the trees close by, not the ones down on the Weald which usually look so good at this time of year.

Thursday, October 28th
What a day! The nose bleed that started a couple of days ago is still going strong and the doctor had to come this morning and bung it up with wadding. The whole trouble at present is that my blood won't clot. Even after injections it won't clot, and so every now and again I get a nasty surprise after an injection. We won't elaborate on the theme. It just remains to be said that I have been fairly worried by my state of health these last couple of days. It is fairly late in the afternoon, four o'clock to be precise, and I am feeling rather tired. I was complaining about lack of occupation for my hands yesterday. This afternoon had been taken up wholly with model making. Angela brought back with her from Oxford a model of the 'Victory'.

Saturday, October 30th

For some reason I missed yesterday, the twenty-ninth. I could have sworn that I wrote yesterday, but coming to think of it, I spent most of yesterday asleep. It is sad that I should have missed yesterday, but there we are. My nose is still bleeding in both nostrils and I seem to be bleeding everywhere else. The doctor said as I am so anaemic it is affecting the clotting mechanism of the rest of me, but I won't bore you with all my ailments; let's just pray that they sort themselves out. With faith all is possible, as I keep on saying, but all I need is that faith. I apologize for my writing; for some reason it is not quite as it should be.

Sunday, October 31st

Last night was spent much more comfortably. I didn't wake up half as much as I did the night before, and I think my nose may have settled down a bit, but we shall see this morning. The doctor is coming (I fear just to change the plugs, but anything is better than nothing I reckon). There – you have had all my gripes for this morning. Now I will try and find some more cheery subject.

Yesterday I prayed with M. in the evening and it was the first time prayer had come naturally and easily for quite a few days. I got somewhere and it was a very rewarding feeling. She was praying at the same time, but neither of us knew it, so it was very rewarding indeed. Life drags by slowly during this illness, and everyone is so kind that I feel in many ways I am letting them down by not being more pleasant and cheerful. Nothing is wasted on me; people will just sit for hours, not talking but being company. It is the presence that counts.

At the moment I have no one with me but I have my book. No one will ever be able to read this as I am writing it pretty well completely horizontal. What I would do without this book I hate to think. It absorbs an awful lot of my feelings which would otherwise be lavished on innocent bystanders. I can't understand why my writing should have been affected by my illness, which without doubt it has. The trouble is that I don't dare sit up as I am worried that my nose will start all over again. It is a great triumph getting it to stop bleeding and I don't want to test it.

The doctor arrived and made what I reckon was a right mess of my nose, but you can't blame him, because it is a curse and refuses to stop bleeding.

Monday, November 1st

There is very little to say today except that the doctor came and had a look at the old snout and decided to leave the disgusting bungs in until tomorrow. The time is five past five and I have spent the whole of the day asleep. I hate to think what tonight is going to be like. He has decided to call in a specialist to look at my nose. I do hope they find out the problem and cure it.

Tuesday, November 2nd

Yesterday was spent entirely in sleep, except for the little time I spent writing. P. came, I haven't the faintest idea when, but it was very pleasant as it meant that the whole day passed quickly and I wasn't bored at all. I wonder what to-day will bring. The doctor comes late morning and a nose specialist is coming in the evening. I do hope he can sort something out for me. I think I have said all that before — all apologies if I have, but I can't remember a word of what I wrote yesterday. All very much along the same track I should think, worrying terribly about myself.

One shouldn't pray for one's own recovery, *it is obvious* one should pray that one is doing God's will. God never wills that one should be ill and in pain, but he brings good out of evil, and the way he does it is his will. I must just let myself relax into his care and be content that I am doing, or trying to do, his will. I shouldn't even have to try.

There, I have been interrupted again, this time by the newspaper which is its usual boring self. Full of spicy court cases between millionaires, compulsive stuff for a chap like me. I am going to keep on writing until my breakfast arrives. I wish it would hurry up. I only asked for Farley's Rusks and coffee. That could only take a couple of minutes, but so far it has taken about half an hour.

I have managed to do one thing with this illness, and that is to turn myself into a cabbage or a vegetable. As long as there is company around I can lie on my back and not think about anything, in fact just vegetate. If M. is vacuuming the room, or P. modelling, that is fine; I can just lie there and pass occasional remarks and they need only be very occasional. It is just the fact of the company that counts and allows me to vegetate. If it wasn't for Angela's model I really don't know how time would have passed, not that I have done hardly any of it, but having P. there doing it passes the time. He is tremendous company. I don't know what I would have done without him, and he has the Headmaster's permission to stay away from the school and be at home while I am not well. It is rotten on him that this should have happened on his half term. The marvellous thing about the model is that it is pleasing to look at. He has enjoyed doing it and I have enjoyed his company. It was the perfect gift.

What is going to happen when it is all finished, or rather what isn't going to happen? Can we possibly launch into another model? I reckon it all depends on my nose. A lot rests on you, my bashed-up smelly friend. I don't know if I can even call you a friend; you have been nothing but a pest, and for the last few days you have been a useless pest at that.

P. has been in the room all afternoon and he has been busily modelling while I just lie here and watch him. It is an extraordinary pleasant way of passing the time, and now he returns with tea. Just to say that M. and Helena have gone to the dentist. I haven't the faintest idea when they will be back, but I do hope it is before the new specialist arrives. Time really has moved this afternoon, God bless it. It is very nearly five o'clock and the doctor is due here at 6.30, so I haven't all that long to wait. It is so kind of them to come out and see me after hours as it were. I mustn't forget that at this time both could probably be at home.

Wednesday, November 3rd

The specialist arrived yesterday, and unfortunately all he did was to change the bungs, but what he also did was give Robin (the doctor) and myself confidence – so much for him. Yesterday P. finished the 'Victory' which was a great success and today we are faced with the making of a 12th Century plough from very rough plans. Yesterday after the specialist had been to re-bung my nose I had hopes that all bleeding had stopped, but I started it again by trying to breath through my nose in my sleep with closed mouth. That could be the cause, because it only ever bleeds at night. There you have my complaints for the day; but it doesn't matter, because I know that I am doing God's will, because I have a desire to do God's will, and this is the only way in which I can do it, and therefore I cannot fail to be doing it.

Saturday, November 6th

This morning something very disturbing is happening. I get little pink clouds with a hole in the middle floating in front of my left eye. No amount of rubbing or anything will remove it at all. It isn't worrying, it is just eye-catching, which isn't surprising considering its point of origin!

Well, the doctor decided to leave the bungs where they are, and though I am disappointed, I am apt to agree with him. The only thing that annoys me is that I will have to spend another sleepless night, with God's help all is possible. M. isn't too pleased, she expected them to be removed.

I lie here waiting for my favourite part of the evening when she and P. come in to the study and we all read the New Testament, or rather M. does, and we say a few prayers. It makes praying so pleasant and it is for some reason very refreshing.

I do wish she would hurry up and come down because I am beginning to feel very sleepy and I won't be in a fit state for the best part of the evening.

Wednesday, November 10th

I will tell you exactly what will happen today. In about ten minutes I will have breakfast, which will last me a few minutes, and when that is over P. will come in and we will spend the rest of the day doing the model, with the very occasional break. I am allowing boredom to get the upper hand. I am sorry; what would I do if I didn't have P. to keep me company? My main trouble at present is that I have lost most urges to read, write or learn, so I am left to modelling, which I can't really do because of the confinements of my bed, so I have to lie and watch Pa.

I don't think it will be long before I start to try and be mobile; that will be the day.

Thursday, November 11th

Yesterday P. brought me the most marvellous present called Plasticraft. One can enmould in plastic, very nearly anything, and so today has been a wild search for things to enmould. . . It is more difficult than one thinks.

Saturday, November 13th

Yesterday was a very bad day. I spent most of it feeling pretty ill, hence the gap. Today is different. I feel better and much more full of life. Well you are getting your contribution, aren't you! So you have no reason to complain.

I wish I could conjure back the days when, having nothing to do, I could sit down and write ten or twelve pages with the greatest of ease.

Sunday, November 14th
Yesterday afternoon was absolutely disastrous as far as the plastic hobby went. Everything went wrong. I couldn't list the accidents that occurred, but the result was that P. and I were pretty short of temper by the time the afternoon was over. Today we take on outside contracts, so I hope for greater success, because I don't want to go round mucking up other peoples' preciousnesses.

The Vicar arrived this morning as is his custom to take communion. For some reason it was a very joyful communion.

My stomach, which isn't up to scratch, is ruling the roost at the moment.

I wonder what life is like at Wye. I hadn't thought of it for a long time. I don't miss it at all. It is interesting to wonder how things will turn out, or where I will be led – I certainly haven't the faintest idea, and I presume I have given up caring. It must all lead somewhere.

Monday, November 15th
This morning was spent polishing up the backs of one or two of our plasticraft efforts, which were a much greater success than we possibly hoped for. Also I started to make a lamp-shade, but that has ground to a halt owing to ham-fistedness.

What do people do who are bed-ridden for years – there must be something that stops them going completely cabbage-like?

Tuesday, November 16th
The best way I can think of starting the fourth volume is by asking you how you would start if faced by the same problem. I know you will give me no answer as usual, but I will not blame you or be cross with you. I am used to your silence; in fact, I am very grateful for it.

There – I have broached the problem and another

volume is in motion for good or for bad. I am forgetting who this is dedicated to; of course, it is for God. I feel as if I have written long and very profoundly but I look back; not much there, is there? That I find is one of the sad things about writing, you tax your brain and the result is always so small and insignificant.

I didn't tell you that P. brought back two old clocks, first for the fun of dismantling them and secondly for the plasticraft. So we dismantled one of them last night and have spent this morning cleaning endless cogs and setting them in plastic. We are beginning to overdo it rather, but the fun of it is great and the finished product decorative and satisfying.

Last night at three thirty, M. and I woke up and had a cup of tea until half past four, and then read until half past five. Consequently I am a little tired now, and they are using it as an excuse for a forced rest this afternoon. This, to my disgust, means that nothing will get done this afternoon at all. Much as I am against the rest, I need it, I am tired.

What is it about sympathy that cuts against the grain so much? I have just come in for a bit and found myself boiling up inside against the giver, which is entirely wrong – I can't fathom the feeling.

Wednesday, November 17th
Today has been so busy in its way that this book, this precious Journal, has got left to the very end, just before I fold up for the night. It has been one of those fully occupied days.

This Spiritual Journal has degenerated again, but there is nothing that can be done because I am not being spiritually stimulated by any book or thoughts. It doesn't worry me because I know it is only a passing phase, as has always been the case up to now, and the recording of such periods of spiritual dryness I presume is the function of a Spiritual Journal.

156

As a passing note, Maria had one puppy today, which died, which is very sad. Surprisingly I forgot that because Helena has been so looking forward to them; not only her, but Maria as well.

Thursday, November 18th

A long day ending late. By that I don't mean that I am in any way dis-satisfied with the day, on the contrary. This morning was taken up by Plasticraft.

Saturday, November 20th

You are going to get very little today, you lucky people, as it is late and I feel a little tired and ill. The latter is due to the fact that I have had my bungs removed. Strange that I should feel ill, but there is a clot up my nose which is making me feel sick. It is blessing enough that the bungs have gone, without my complaining. Not complaining is very difficult. Maybe the doctor will be able to help tomorrow when he comes in the morning, but I doubt it.

P. has just been seized by a model-makers frenzy and is busy making Trevethick's Engine at ten o'clock, but I won't complain because this is normally a very quiet dull time of evening, and having him around livens things up; it doesn't disturb my literary efforts either.

Sunday, November 21st

The end of yet another unproductive day. It has passed without me really doing anything and yet it hasn't been a dull day by any manner of means. My nose has kept me a little quiet and threatens to do so for the next few days, but I think it may be worth it in the long run, it has been getting better and better all day I think.

Waking up in the morning is always a little unpleasant and that is the time I dislike most, but never mind, if my nose is mending, it is all very much worth it. That's about all I can think of saying this Sunday. It seems extraordinary to me that I can pass through a whole day and only have that to say at the end, but that was my day, very roughly, not very exciting but passable. I am glad it is over – very nearly anyway.

Monday, November 22nd

My writing this morning is going to be pretty shocking, because I am lying almost completely flat, with my book miles away from me, because my knees, which are my only support, are rather a long way away from me as well. At present I am surprisingly tired. I say surprisingly, as I spent most of this afternoon asleep, and that usually stilts my evening form to some degree. I am going to stop writing for a while otherwise I will never get a chance to say my own prayers, which have become very small since we started saying communal prayers, but it doesn't matter.

There, I am back. What I am learning is to leave everything to Him emotionally, spiritually, organisationally, everything; all I have to do is his will, which is let him do everything. It should be so easy, and as a matter of fact I think that it is getting easier, but I will have to be on my guard against false emotions which I find so rampant in my effort. There is the key; it should be his effort, but I feel sure that something must come from me. Is it obedience? What is it?

The whole thing is rather complex. I know he will show me the way, it is just a matter of patience.

As nothing else is happening I will give you a medical report. Things seem to be brightening up and I am hoping they may clear up entirely quite soon. There, that is all. It is time for reading and prayers also, and I am very glad and tired.

Tuesday, November 23rd

Today has passed yet again uneventfully, but satisfactorily. I had the blood clots removed from my nose, and bungs blessedly put in their place – I couldn't put up with the clots any longer. To take over from my nose, my left arm has begun to hurt. I now feel that I have been writing for ages, but I know if I read through I will be very disappointed. Also every time I let the pen rest for more than ten seconds, I go to sleep. I must stop now and try to say some prayers before I completely pass out.

Wednesday, November 24th
Most of today has been passed in sleep, and enjoyable, gentle work on the plasticraft set. I have been sleeping because I have been having pills for my arm which has mysteriously started hurting, along with my right knee. In many ways my knees and arms are more of a nuisance than my nose, which I have got in a morbid sort of way used to. I accept it in its monotony. I hope it isn't because I am getting sorry for myself. I am not sorry for myself at present, only self centred. Now I am doing something even worse, being pleased with myself, pleasant for me – that comforting feeling inside. God, help me to leave all the fighting to you.

Thursday, November 25th
Tonight I have left my writing far too late, and everything I do turns to sleep, so I won't be writing at all. This is all you are getting.

William died in the afternoon of the following day.

Postscript

I am sorry now that when the time came for that final illness I did not tell William that he was going to die. It was a lack of faith and understanding on my part. I underestimated him and also the love and purposes of God.

I feared he would despair, once he knew that things could only get worse—that death was all that he had to look forward to. I was caught in old thought patterns, and I was wrong. By then death was *not* all that he had to look forward to at all. He loved God and was triumphantly on his way home. I believe now that the truth about his illness would have relieved him of his endless struggle to get well against insuperable odds, and of the repeated disappointment of his failures.

If I had told him he was dying we would have seen great things. He could, and I think he would, have accepted each stage of the disease as it progressed, as steps forward on his way, a progressive release. But as it was he fought valiantly on, perhaps for some unnecessary weeks.

I hope his writing will be a comfort to others. Because he didn't know he was dying, he didn't write about that, but about his journey towards God. And that is living.

Rosemary Attlee
Kent, England, Spring, 1984